EMPTY BREADBASKET?

The Coming Challenge to America's
Food Supply and What We Can Do About It

A Study of the U.S. Food System by
The Cornucopia Project of Rodale Press

33 East Minor Street
Emmaus, Pennsylvania 18049
Phone: (215) 967-5171

Contents

Page

Preface...v

Current and Possible Directions for
the U.S. Food System....................................1
    1. Scenario 1: Crash..................................3
    2. Scenario 2: Soft Landing/Abundance................6

The Challenge.......................................9
    1. The Success and Vulnerabilities of the U.S. Food System...11
    2. Economic Structure...............................15
    3. Food Transport..................................28
    4. Land Use/Soil Abuse.............................31
    5. Monoculture....................................37
    6. Energy...41
    7. Mineral Base...................................50
    8. Environmental Impacts...........................56
    9. Water..58
    10. Climate.......................................66
    11. Nutrition/Health...............................71
    12. Food Processing...............................74
    13. Fisheries.....................................77
    14. Forest Resources..............................80
    15. Urban Food Systems............................83
    16. Food Assistance...............................85
    17. International Dimensions.......................89

What We Can Do About It...............................95
    1. Goals for the U.S. Food System..................97

iv   **Contents**

2. The Cornucopia Agenda: Finding the Path
   to Food Security................................100
      a. Farmers................................101
      b. Consumers..............................103
      c. Food Industry..........................105
      d. Cities.................................107
      e. States................................111
      f. United States.........................118
3. Summary/Conclusions..........................127
4. Notes.......................................128

Appendix....................................155
   1. Cornucopia Op-Ed Ads......................157
   2. Background and Acknowledgements...........168

Preface

The U.S. food system is the most productive the world has ever seen. Ironically, it is also one of the most destructive systems of all time. To provide our food abundance, we are burning up natural resources: soil, water, energy. In the midst of plenty, we seem bent on devastating our potential for future productivity.

In 1980, Rodale Press initiated The Cornucopia Project to study the entire U.S. food system. The goal was to document where our system is vulnerable, and then to suggest how the system could be transformed to sustain and conserve our resources. This report contains the results of that study.

Current and Possible Directions for the U.S. Food System

Scenario 1: Crash

Soil erosion has eliminated about half of the originally productive farmland in the United States. Drought, lack of soil conservation measures, and continuous row cropping have led to erosion levels far worse than in the dust bowl years of the 1930's. Deserts in the western U.S. continue to expand. Billions of dollars are spent each year to remove soil from streams and waterways. Many reservoirs and hydroelectric dams have completely silted up.

All prime farmland near metropolitan regions has been built on or paved over. In Texas, Nebraska, Kansas, California and Arizona, large areas of irrigated farmland have been abandoned because of exhausted water supplies, soaring pumping costs, or high salinity. Little land is available to grow export crops.

Heavy fertilizer use is mandatory on all crops because remaining soils are lifeless mediums bereft of productivity. The U.S. supply of phosphates is depleted, and we must purchase this fertilizer mineral from OPEC—the Organization of Phosphate Exporting Countries—which consists of Morocco, Jordan, Egypt, and Saudi Arabia. We also import much of our nitrogen fertilizer.

Pesticides and herbicides are used so heavily and repeatedly that their application is almost continuous. Several species of formerly common animals become extinct each year. Occupational diseases reduce farm workers' life expectancy to below 50 years.

Despite the heavy use of chemicals, insect damage increases substantially. Herbicide-resistant weeds compete with food crops and reduce productivity. New bugs take hold in the U.S. and destroy significant portions of the harvest. Since only a few varieties of major crops are grown, a new strain of rust destroys half the Midwest wheat

3

harvest. Coastal areas are over-fished and polluted, and total fish harvest is down 50 percent.

The nation's petroleum supply is dangerously short. Food processing and packaging use three times as much energy as food production. The fuel needed to plow, cultivate, harvest and transport food is often unavailable. Natural gas for production of nitrogen fertilizer is scarce and the price skyrockets. Earlier in this decade, before our domestic supply of oil and gas was depleted, foreign oil was cut off by a Mideast war. As it was, however, the U.S. could no longer meet its imported fuel bill.

Coal is now the predominant fuel. Montana, Idaho, Wyoming, West Virginia and Pennsylvania have been extensively strip-mined. Because of extensive fossil fuel use, carbon dioxide levels in the atmosphere have increased dramatically. The planet's temperature has risen 2° C., and dry land farming is difficult in Oklahoma, Iowa, and Kansas. Acid rain has killed most fresh water lakes in the eastern U.S. Forests are cut down to provide firewood. Solid waste disposal costs the U.S. $5 billion annually.

The family farm has virtually disappeared, and only a few prosperous small towns remain. There is a sort of modern feudalism in the rural areas of the country, where social classes are sharply divided between those who work on the land, those who manage it, and those who own it. Land prices are so high only large corporations can buy it, and average farm size is 2,000 acres. Farm productivity continues to decrease, and most of our food is grown on about 10,000 highly automated megafarms.

Fewer people work on farms and in the food system as a whole. Consumers buy 90 percent of their groceries from three supermarket chains. National strikes of supermarket workers occur periodically. To reduce spoilage and minimize handling problems, these stores have eliminated fresh produce, and sell only highly processed foods. New food businesses are nearly impossible to start because capital is in short supply and interest rates are more than 25 percent.

Malnutrition is rampant throughout the country. Fresh food consumption has been reduced to negligible levels. More than half the population is on food stamps, and the annual cost of the program approaches $50 billion. Obesity is a problem for 80 percent of U.S. women and men between 40 and 60 years of age. Serious vitamin and mineral deficiency affects 20 percent of the population, while many more suffer from "junk food malnourishment." About $15 billion is spent on alcoholic beverages each year.

Almost every major metropolitan area experiences periodic food shortages. Food prices are astronomical—a loaf of bread costs over $10, tomatoes are pushing $3 apiece, and a 10-ounce jar of instant coffee sells for $50. The amount of disposable income spent by the average person on food rises from 20 to 40 percent. The poor are forced to spend as much as 60 to 80 percent of their income on food. The food stores that remain open are heavily guarded, and in many places gardens become impossible to maintain because of thievery.

During food shortages in several places, hungry people panic and loot grocery stores and warehouses. People begin to hoard food and the supply becomes even scarcer, leading to more hoarding. Famine strikes several cities in the eastern U.S., and the national guard is brought in to help distribute food.

Around the world, there are numerous famines after each poor harvest. U.S. food is not available in any large quantities for export. In some places, massive famines occur. Governments break down, and local skirmishes mushroom into wars. International order disintegrates completely.

Scenario 2:
Soft Landing/Abundance

Through the combined efforts of farmers, government programs, and an educated public, soil erosion is reduced to manageable levels. The necessity for silt removal from the nation's waterways is almost eliminated.

Soil building programs are underway throughout the U.S. Millions of acres are being reforested. Expansion of U.S. deserts is checked, and some have become agriculturally productive. Several desert plants are being cultivated for their food or energy value.

Urban sprawl onto prime farmland has been halted through a combination of local, state and federal programs. The nation's prime farmland is declared a national trust and is protected as such. Farmers receive full development rights benefits through tax credits, but land speculators are excluded from this program.

Beef feedlots are decentralized, and brought closer to local grain sources, cutting down on transportation and eliminating the need for energy-intensive grain drying. Most farms grow a variety of crops and animals, so organic wastes are produced close to the fields they fertilize. The animals produce food and fertilizer, and also use rangeland that would otherwise be unproductive.

New crop varieties make dryland farming more profitable in the West and Midwest. The pumping of groundwater for irrigation is brought into balance with the water table's recharge rate. Drip irrigation and other water-conserving techniques are used on all irrigated farmland.

Chemical pesticide use is drastically reduced, having been replaced by biological pest controls. The shift from extensive monocultures to locally adapted varieties reduces insect damage to crops by 20 percent. Occupational hazards of farming are reduced significantly, and the life expectancy of farmworkers begins to exceed the average.

Much of the food system is powered by renewable energy sources. Farms, depending on their local geographical and climatic conditions, use windmills, solar cells, small-scale hydro and cogeneration units to produce electricity. Passive and active solar units, methane and methanol provide heat and portable fuels. Nearly all organic wastes are being used as fertilizer, and chemical fertilizers are seldom needed.

Small family farms are increasing in number as more and more young people—of both sexes—enter farming. Since small farms use resources most efficiently, they can compete successfully with large farms. Rural population increases, and local communities become vibrant developing economic centers. Stable land prices have made speculation impossible.

Malnutrition is rare in the U.S. Extensive education campaigns reduce the sales of junk food, alcohol and tobacco by 50 percent. The incidence of obesity and diet-related diseases is reduced significantly. Consumption of fresh vegetables, fruits and grains increases, while consumption of fat, salt and processed food decreases.

Major metropolitan areas of the country are reorganized to include Departments of Food, which aid and encourage local food production and distribution. Some cities expand their boundaries to include enough farmland so that they are largely self-sufficient. Urban gardens, greenhouses, aquaculture pools, farmers' markets and other food outlets proliferate.

Grocery stores and neighborhood food co-ops contract with local farmers for their food supply. Larger grocery stores install canning, drying and freezing facilities to process food produced by their shoppers. The price of most foods stabilizes, and only produce shipped long distances continues to escalate in real price.

The long distance transport of fresh produce virtually ceases, as production is decentralized and different regions of the country become more self-sufficient in fruit and vegetable production. New crops, such as amaranth, provide increased food diversity. Fresh salad greens from home and neighborhood solar greenhouses are available everywhere throughout the year. Pollution of lakes and rivers is reduced, and fishery yields are managed to assure a renewable supply.

Current and Possible Directions
8   for the U.S. Food System

U.S. food exports decline as developing countries increase their own food self-sufficiency. Famines occur only rarely. Surplus grain produced by the U.S. goes into an International Grain Reserve for disaster or famine relief, or is used to produce energy. World health levels and life expectancy increase dramatically.

*   *   *   *   *   *

These scenarios are not predictions. But neither are they created out of nothing. Both of them suggest real possibilities for America's food future.

The scenario for disaster shows how things could look if we simply extend the trends and problems of the present into the future. But as dismal as this picture is, the reality could be much worse—and may arrive faster than anyone thinks. The U.S. food system, like a rubber band, is being stretched to the extreme. So far it has managed to snap back into its original shape. But the pressures on the system are growing. One day it may be stretched too far, and break.

The scenario for abundance could also become fact. All we need to achieve it is to direct our food system into sustainable paths. The needed changes would not require any new technology or resources. We have the people, and the know-how, to build such a system. All we lack is the will to do it.

The Challenge

1
The Success of the U.S. Food System

The American food system is a productive wonder. Fewer than three percent of our people live on farms,[1] yet they grow enough to feed the United States and provide more than 85 percent of the world's surplus food as well.[2] A farmer of today can produce 33 times more corn per hour of work than a farmer of 60 years ago.[3]

Feeding people is the country's biggest business. Annual food sales now top $300 billion,[4] and the food industry employs 1.7 million workers.[5] In addition, agriculture makes an important contribution to our balance of payments. In 1980 we exported some $40.4 billion worth of food. Our food imports cost $17.3 billion.[6]

U.S. farmers are supported by an extensive agricultural education and research system, which includes the Land Grant Colleges, the state agricultural experiment stations, and the United States Department of Agriculture's Extension Service. These programs reach into all 50 states, produce large numbers of trained workers and perform the research that has transformed the face of agriculture throughout the world. In 1980, the USDA spent over $664 million on research.[7]

The achievements of this research system are staggering. Yields for basic crops have been dramatically increased. Corn yields, for example, have more than doubled since 1945, while potato yields have risen four-fold since 1915.[8] Disease resistance, ability to utilize fertilizer, and drought resistance have been greatly improved for most crops. Animal diseases have been brought under control, and new, more productive varieties of livestock have been developed. Even some vitamins were discovered by agricultural researchers seeking to improve animal feed.

All these factors benefit American consumers, who, on the average, use only 13.6 percent of their personal income for food, compared to as much as 60 percent in some developing countries.[9] Our food is reasonably priced, despite the fact that we enjoy an amazing diversity of fresh food all year. And if one region suffers from drought or crop failure, another region's surplus can be brought in to prevent any calamity.

Our bounty has blessed other nations as well, helping to keep millions of people from starving to death. In the last 25 years, the United States has given close to $30 billion worth of food aid.[10] And we provide much of the developed world with cheap animal feed, helping to hold down the price of meat.

The Vulnerabilities of the U.S. Food System

The U.S. food system grew to greatness because our country was endowed with:

- Seemingly endless fertile land;
- A favorable climate for agriculture;
- Plentiful oil, gas, coal and water power;
- Large number of hard-working people;
- Advancing agricultural technology.

For almost 200 years, these factors combined to work wonders.

But now, the United States' food supply is vulnerable. Even though we still have large crops in years of good weather, the system's future is endangered. Just as we had large quantities of gasoline the day before the oil embargo, we now have substantial stores of surplus food.

But that could change overnight. The average U.S. city has a 2 to 3 day supply of food. Most of America's northeastern states import over 70 percent of their food.[11] Even a slight disruption could cause serious trouble. And if this flow of food were restricted or cut off, the consequences could be catastrophic.

There are, unfortunately, a wide variety of things that could disrupt this tenuous line of supply. A truckers' strike could cut it almost completely. More than 34,000 trucks come into the northeastern United States each *week* to keep it supplied with food.[12] A rail strike would also have a severe impact.

Another oil embargo or shortage would threaten our food supply. During the last oil shortage, grocery warehouses in

Pennsylvania were out of almost 20 percent of their stocks.[13] A study by the U.S. Department of Energy disclosed that a 10 percent reduction in oil supply would result in a 55 percent increase in the price of vegetables and fruits.[14]

Our food supply could be disrupted by a labor dispute in the main areas of production, or a Medfly-like quarantine of these areas, or a drought or other natural catastrophe. Food industry executives now believe that because of union penetration, a national supermarket strike is possible.[15] Added to this already overlong list of threats to our food security must be the possibility of total economic collapse in our farming sector. Farm debt has sky-rocketed in the last decade to over $160 billion—up 290 percent since 1970.[16] A burst in the bubble of land values would bankrupt most of the farmers in the United States. Some observers argue that farmers are already bankrupt, since there is no forseeable way for them to pay off their debts, or to avoid getting deeper in debt.

Finally, we must add the hypothetical and horrible spectre of sabotage to this list. Given the state of terrorism in the world today, this is not unthinkable. Knocking out six bridges across the Mississippi River, for example, could almost stop the flow of food to the Northeast.[17]

Taken individually or in concert, these factors seriously threaten the supply of food in the United States. Unfortunately, they are only the short term threats. A number of systemic "diseases" afflicting the whole food system could, in time, curtail or block our supply of food just as drastically as could these relatively short-range threats. Many people argue that these longer-range threats are the most dangerous, because they are so pervasive.

Among these diseases are the enormous erosion of the country's vital topsoils, the loss of farmland to development, our almost total dependence on a depleting fuel supply that is escalating in price and over which we have little control, our similar dependence on a depleting mineral base, our overuse of dangerous pesticides and soil-damaging synthetic fertilizers, our non-sustainable use of water, the equally non-sustainable environmental impacts our food system is having, the threats to human health of our current diet, and our self-defeating patterns of domestic food assistance and participation in the global food system.

Our food system maintains the illusion of unlimited success. It still feeds us. But the foundation of the system is being eaten away—slowly, quietly, yet surely. The biggest danger is that the situation may become critical before it even seems serious.

14   The Challenge

Taken together, these short- and longer-term threats add up to the most serious challenge our food supply has ever encountered. They endanger our national security. If unchecked, they will lead us to a world similar to that described in Scenario 1.

The best way to demonstrate our predicament is to look at the key parts of our food system one at a time. The following pages do that in detail. This is followed by a list of measures The Cornucopia Project feels are needed to transform our present food system into a sustainable, safe and affordable cornucopia.

2
Economic Structure

The economic structure of our food system is balanced on a tightrope. Without the present price supports, tax write-offs, emergency loan programs, and artificially inflated land values, many U.S. farmers would be bankrupt *right now*. We would fall off this highwire, and the system that feeds us would collapse.

But if we stay on the wire and keep heading in the same direction, the consequences may be equally disastrous. We end up with a food system controlled by a few corporations with almost absolute power over what we eat. And the price we are currently paying to move forward is enormous: loss of farmers, processors, and locally-based grocery stores, devastation of rural communities, soil erosion, and the depletion of non-renewable resources.

It is unlikely that there is any conspiracy to destroy our food system, or to control food production, distribution and prices. But sometimes the system seems to act as if there were. And it has come to the point that the structure of our system no longer serves the best interests of anyone—farmers, food companies, or consumers.

Farming

Since 1920, more than two-thirds of all U.S. farms have disappeared.[1] Between 1950 and 1970, we lost 100,000 small farms annually, or nearly 2000 each week.[2] Since then the loss has slowed somewhat, but it still continues. We now have about two million farms, of which about 20 percent produce 80 percent of the nation's food and fiber.[3] The largest 7 percent of U.S. farms

15

NUMBER OF U.S. FARMS AND AVERAGE SIZE OF FARMS

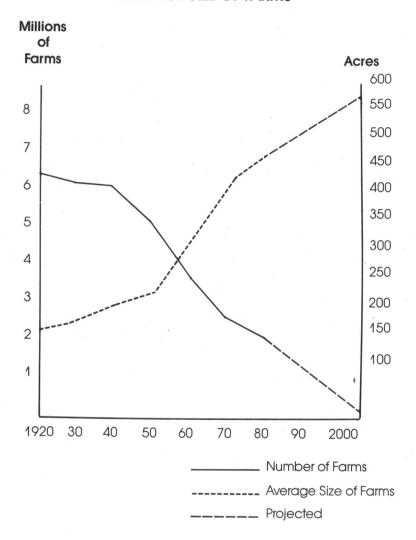

Sources: U.S. Department of Agriculture, *1979 Handbook of Agricultural Charts,* Agricultural Handbook No. 561, p. 29. U.S. Government Printing Office, Washington, D.C. 20250.

U.S., Department of Agriculture, *Agricultural Statistics 1980,* pp. 417, 418. U.S. Government Printing Office, Washington, D.C. 20250.

receive over 50 percent of the total cash receipts from the sale of farm products.[4]

Studies have shown that the most efficient farm production unit is not the large corporate spread, but the basic family farm.[5] Yet farms—and farm suppliers—keep getting bigger. Average farm size has tripled over the last 60 years, from 150 to 450 acres.[6] Based on 1978 data, the USDA found that one percent of farmland owners control 30 percent of all U.S. farmland.[7] A related report projected that if present trends continue to the end of the century, one percent of America's farms will control half our food and fiber production.[8]

Similarly, fifteen companies account for 60 percent of all inputs to farm production.[9] Four companies now sell 80 percent of all combines; two companies sell 79 percent of all cotton pesticides; two companies sell 50 percent of all corn herbicides, and four companies sell 75 percent of all tractors sold in America.[10]

Current laws encourage the trend toward giantism. Tax policies favor large operators, and subsidy programs benefit the largest producers most. In 1978, nearly half the total U.S. farm commodity payments of $2.03 billion went to just 10 percent of the farmers— those with the biggest farms. Half the farmers—those with the smallest farms—received only about 10 percent of the payments.[11]

Hidden subsidies may also favor farmers in one region or area. California agriculture, which now supplies more than 40 percent of the country's fresh produce,[12] has received a multi-billion dollar subsidy through federal water and irrigation projects. Estimates are that nearly 20 million acres of agricultural land in the East have gone out of production as a direct result of federally-funded projects in the West.[13]

Along with the increase in farm size has come an increasing dependence on technology. A new technology is usually measured against the sole criteria of short-term economic efficiency. If it passes this simplistic test it is usually adopted. New, super-large tractors and harvesters, for example, argue persuasively for larger and larger farms. Once these behemoths are purchased, the farmer must expand his operation so that these expensive machines do not stand idle. Ever-larger farm machinery impels ever larger farms, leading to more soil erosion (large machines cannot handle soil conserving terraces and contours), increased soil compaction, more fuel use, fewer farmers, and a more vulnerable, fragile agriculture.

NUMBER OF LARGE
(VALUE OF SALES OVER $200,000) FARMS

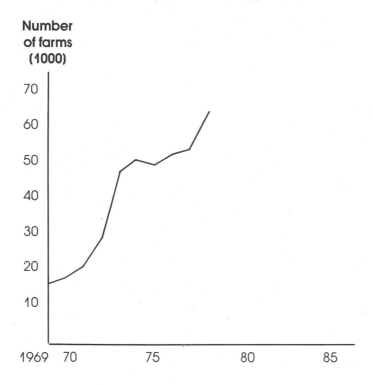

Number
of farms
(1000)

Source: U.S., Department of Agriculture, *Farm Income Statistics,* National
         Economics Division, Economics, Statistics and Cooperative Service,
         Washington, D.C., October, 1979, p. 52.

The cost of this large machinery has also helped contribute to increasing farm debt. Despite the vast wealth of the U.S., the richness of our soils, and our technological know-how, many farmers are in dangerous financial shape. Farm debt is now over $160 billion, a rise of 650 percent in the last 20 years.[14] That's an *average* of over *$68,000* for every farmer in the United States.[15] Predictions are that if current trends continue until 1990, farm debt will reach $600 billion.[16]

The farmer is pushed into ever-increasing debt through a variety of structural factors. Perhaps because of a previously bad year or because he wishes to "get ahead" and expand his operation, the farmer borrows at the beginning of the year to finance the seeds, fuel, fertilizer, and pesticides needed to farm. If he has a poor harvest, this debt cannot be fully repaid, and the next year he will have to borrow even more. Then he has to earn at least 10 to 15 percent more each year—whatever the inflation rate is—just to break even. Once in this downward spiral, it is difficult to escape.

Ironically this debt cycle would probably have ended long ago without runaway inflation. It works like this: In order to stay in business the farmer has to borrow more money from the bank. To borrow this money he needs more collateral. Inflation, which drives the price of his land over higher, gives him that increasing collateral. Without skyrocketing farmland prices (since 1970 farmland values have increased an average of 245 percent[17]) the farmer would not be able to finance next year's operations, or refinance his old debt, or make payments on outstanding debts. Bankruptcy could easily result.

If the inflating bubble of land prices burst, as some economists are forecasting, or even if land inflation leveled off, many farmers would be left holding huge debts with little collateral or no additional equity. There would be no way to refinance or borrow money for next year's crop. This is basically what happened in the U.S. in the 1920's. Farmland values plummeted and it took nearly 25 years for prices to return to former levels.

Inflated land values have given many farmers windfall profits, and have attracted land speculators, which has driven the price of land up even further. Commenting on this situation, noted agricultural economist, Harold Breimyer says: "It is an enormous paper profit. Its benefits are brief and false and confined to a few. Its harm can be excruciating for many when the bubble bursts. No real wealth is created by a chain letter game, a lottery, or speculation in land. Any nation that tries to build upon such manipulation is headed for trouble."[18]

The potential tragedy doesn't stop here, however. Farm loans come from banks, usually smaller rural ones. These banks have outstanding loans from larger banks. If the small banks are forced to call in their debts and confiscate the farms that they now own, it is entirely possible that because of the unavailability of capital, or the lack of qualified buyers, or the deflation of land values, they would not be able to re-sell these properties at a price that would amortize their debt. When this happened during the Great Depression, bank failures resulted. Today there are safeguards to prevent massive bank failures, but they cannot prevent farm failures.

UNITED STATES FARM DEBT

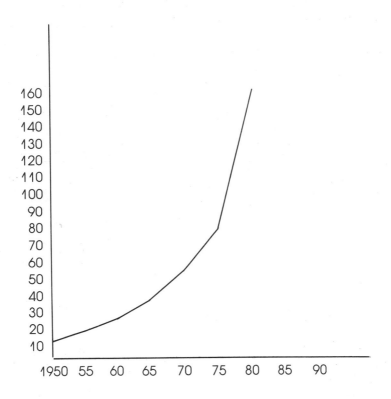

Sources: U.S., Department of Agriculture, *Agricultural Statistics 1980,* pp. 477, 483. U.S. Government Printing Office, Washington, D.C.

U.S. Department of Agriculture, *1979 Handbook of Agricultural Charts,* Agricultural Handbook No. 561, p. 10, chart 12. U.S. Government Printing Office, Washington, D.C.

While farm debt has been soaring, income has been declining. Between 1979 and 1980, diesel fuel prices doubled. Since 1967, feed costs are up 104 percent, seed is up 186 percent, machinery is up 189 percent, and fertilizers are up 193 percent.[19] Gross farm income in 1980 rose about 6 percent to $140 billion, but because of rising costs net income plunged about 29 percent to $22 billion—the largest one-year drop in 50 years.[20]

These rising costs have made it extremely difficult for new farmers to get started. Often, only large corporations or large farm-

CAPITAL REQUIRED TO START A NEW FARM

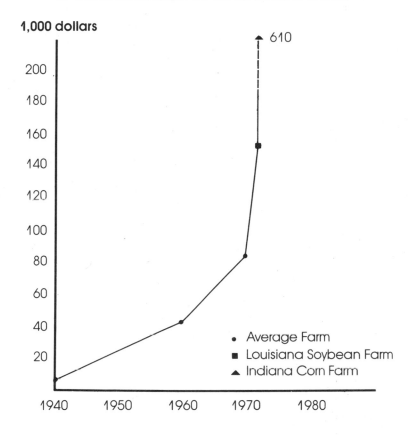

Source: General Accounting Office, *Food, Agriculture and Nutrition Issues For Planning*, (Washington, D.C.: General Accounting Office, June 11, 1980), p. 39.

ers can afford the entry fees. A 1978 study reported that to start a farm that would generate gross sales of $40,000 to $60,000 a year, a person would need a capital investment of $573,000 for a livestock spread, or $285,000 to start a fruit and nut orchard.[21] (The farmer's income would be some part of the gross sales.) These figures are for small farms; the authors of the study suggest that if the farmer had little equity in the land and didn't have off-farm income, he would barely survive financially.

One effect of these structural changes has been a decline in farming quality and in rural life. More and more farmland is owned by absentee landlords. Technology is being substituted for farming knowledge. The farmer has become a machine operator, instead of the agronomist/ecologist/geneticist, etc., that he once was. In the last 20 years, over half of America's farmland has changed ownership, so the intimate knowledge of the land that skilled farmers need is increasingly being lost.

When the number of farmers decreases, farm suppliers eventually go out of business and the rural community suffers. Schools, roads, and other public services deteriorate. The remaining residents are left with an increased tax burden, a decaying community, and little new economic opportunity.

In the face of these massive problems, U.S. farmers have continued to produce abundant harvests. But the structure that should support them is crushing many smaller farmers. As control passes into fewer and fewer hands, competition is reduced, and our food production system becomes less responsive to individual needs and less resilient in times of stress.

Food Industry

Food is America's biggest business. The food and fiber industries employ between 14 and 17 million workers.[22] In 1980, American consumers spent $302.3 billion on food, $1400 for every person in the country. About $80 billion—26 percent—paid for meals out, while the rest was spent for food at home.[23]

In recent years, food costs, like other living expenses, have risen considerably: 10 percent in 1978; 10.9 percent in 1979; and 8.6 percent in 1980.[24] But despite these jumps, food remains a relative bargain. Only 13.6 percent of America's personal spending goes for food, as compared to over 20 percent in France and Sweden, 30 percent in Spain and Italy, and nearly 60 percent in India.[25] And the percentage of disposable income consumers pay for food has declined by almost one-third since 1929.[26]

Our food dollars purchase an amazing variety of edibles. Fifty years ago, most of our grandparents ate strawberries and lettuce in the summer, cabbage and apples in winter, and oranges on special occasions. Today we can buy nearly any food we want almost any time of the year.

Despite its impressive achievements, however, the way the food industry has grown over the years has created some problems, not only for the long-term health of the industry itself, but for the nation's food system as a whole.

THE SUDDEN SLIDE IN FARMERS' FORTUNES

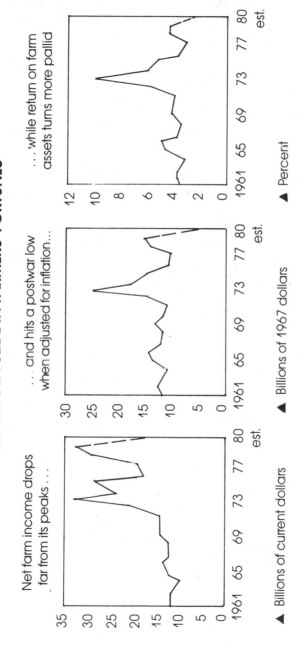

Net farm income drops
far from its peaks....

...and hits a postwar low
when adjusted for inflation...

...while return on farm
assets turns more pallid

▲ Billions of current dollars   ▲ Billions of 1967 dollars   ▲ Percent

Source: "Rippling troubles from the farm belt," *Business Week*, July 14, 1980, p. 94.

One problem is the trend toward consolidation that has occurred in farming, manufacturing, processing and distribution. Currently, there are more than 12,000 food manufacturing plants in the country that employ at least 20 people.[27] But just 49 companies account for 68 percent of all food processing, and 44 companies control over 77 percent of all wholesale and retail revenues.[28] Less than 21 percent of the food stores in the United States are supermarkets, yet these stores accounted for more than 77 percent of 1980 sales.[29]

This consolidation is especially pronounced with particular products. Three companies share 85 percent of the North American banana market. Four bottlers sell 89 percent of the U.S.'s soft drinks. Four firms make 91 percent of the country's cereal. Three brewers produce over half our beer.[30] And just one company makes 90 percent of our canned soup.[31]

The movement toward corporate oligarchy has some potentially dangerous side-effects. It limits efficiency, especially in the use of energy. Many giant companies do their processing in a few, huge plants, rather than in smaller, regional operations. Food is often moved a considerable distance before processing, then shipped back across the country afterwards.

The bigger the company, the less able it is to respond to individual needs, or to adapt to changing circumstances. Recently, for example, a major food company identified with dairy products announced it would no longer sell any natural cheeses. The reason: the company could not afford to hold that much product in inventory to permit the natural aging process to occur.[32]

Pressured by high interest rates, the need to keep inventory turning over, and the imperative to keep manufacturing operations productive, the company decided to withdraw natural cheese and focus on higher-profit items. The practical result is that consumers who want this cheese must now look elsewhere, and probably pay more for imported natural cheese that has travelled thousands of miles. Ironically, many of the small companies that could produce natural cheese profitably have been bought out or driven out of business by larger firms.

Short-term financial considerations were also behind a 1979 decision by the country's primary soup maker that all tomatoes for its New Jersey factory would henceforth be purchased in California and Ohio, and brought east as paste. It had become uneconomic to buy Jersey tomatoes and process them locally.[33]

FIGURE 1

PERCENTAGE OF THE FOOD MANUFACTURING ASSETS OWNED BY THE 50 LARGEST FIRMS

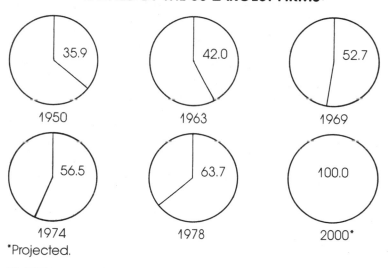

35.9	42.0	52.7
1950	1963	1969
56.5	63.7	100.0
1974	1978	2000*

*Projected.

Source: John M. Connor, *The U.S. Food and Tobacco Industry*, U.S., Department of Agriculture. Agricultural Economic Report #451, p. 12.

Once these corporate decisions are made, and procedures are established, it is very difficult to make rapid changes. For example, in the event of a sudden oil shortage, or a Medfly invasion, long supply and distribution lines could be cut, and there would be no structures in place to help create a regional food system. Major food companies, which would have the capital to develop such structures, might take months or years to get reoriented. During the process, consumers would suffer, and the companies themselves would experience severe difficulties, and perhaps even go under.

Consolidation also tends to limit competition, and may lead to higher food prices. In a controversial food industry study, Russell Parker, a Federal Trade Commission economist, and John Connor, a USDA economist, attempted to compute the extra amount that consumers pay because of the lack of competition. Their estimate for 1980 was over $18 billion.[34] A study by two University of Wisconsin economists suggests that supermarket monopolies have inflated prices another $1 billion annually.[35]

A primary reason large food companies tend to buy up smaller companies is that sales growth in the food industry is unusually difficult. In many businesses, companies can expand without jeopardizing other firms because the potential market is unlimited.But that is not the case with food. Most people do not increase their consumption of food each year. And the natural population increase, by itself, is limited. So in order for a company to grow, it must buy other companies, or increase its market share by displacing another company's product to some extent.

As a result, food companies advertise heavily. The food marketing system is the largest user of national media advertising, buying more than twice as much as its nearest competitor, the automotive/gasoline industry.[36] Estimates are that in 1979 the industry spent from $7 to $9 billion on promotion. About $5 billion of this amount went for "pull" advertising, which is aimed at influencing consumers, while the remainder paid for "push" advertising directed to distributors. Advertising accounts for 3 to 4 cents of every dollar spent on food in grocery stores.[37]

Not all foods receive an equal amount of advertising. Throughout the 1970's, highly processed foods—which have high profit margins—have accounted for most of the total advertising budget. Perishable foods, such as unprocessed meats, poultry and fish, fruits and vegetables, and dairy products take over half of the consumer's food-at-home dollar, but they account for less than 8 percent of the national media advertising. In contrast, breakfast cereal, soft drinks, candy and other desserts, oils and salad dressings, coffee, and prepared foods take only about 20 percent of the consumer food dollar, yet they account for about half of all media advertising.[38]

Major food companies not only control a large share of food sales, they also specify the production techniques used by farmers. Food companies almost always demand a standardized product, and suggest the use of large amounts of chemical pesticides and fertilizers, and expensive machines for picking and processing.[39]

For cosmetic purposes, they demand a particular look as well. Unfortunately, such a system often requires fruit and vegetables to meet arbitrary beauty or size standards, which result in considerable waste as edible—but homely—food is rejected. About one-fourth of all fruits and vegetables picked in this country never make it out of the supermarket.[40]

The food industry, with its current structure, meets the basic food needs of most of us. But under increasing financial pressure, companies are being forced to act for short-term profits, without due regard for such things as the conservation of resources and the sustainability of the food system as a whole. The more consolidated the food industry becomes, the more inflexible and vulnerable our food supply becomes. If these trends are not reversed, Americans may soon have little to say about the cost—or the choice—of the food they eat.

3
Food Transport

America's investment in transportation is immense. We have 3.8 million miles of roads, 178 thousand miles of main-line railroad track,[1] and 25 thousand miles of navigable inland rivers and canals.[2] There are more than 100 million cars and 32 million trucks in the country—three vehicles for every five people. We spend more than $30 billion ($150 per person) each year for highways, burn up 125 billion gallons of gasoline driving on them, and pay $60 billion for commercial truck and railroad services. Transportation uses $165 billion worth of petroleum annually, 53 percent of the total U.S. consumption.[3]

The U.S. Department of Agriculture conservatively estimates that 5.3 percent of the retail cost of food pays for rail and truck transportation. Based on this figure, Americans paid almost $16 billion in 1980 to move their food around.[4] And this does not account for transportation to and from the supermarket, nor the hidden costs such as highway construction and maintenance, deaths and disabilities from transportation accidents, air quality control programs and air pollution-induced illnesses. A U.S. Department of Defense study estimated that the average molecule of processed food in this country travels 1300 miles before being eaten.[5]

Most large shipments of food go by truck, train or barge. While railroads and barges are the most energy-efficient modes of transport, trucks are most commonly used.[6] Except for long distance shipment of grains, trucking dominates the food freight business, transporting 99 percent of all livestock, 88 percent of fresh fruits and vegetables, and more than 80 percent of fresh and frozen meats, dairy products, bakery goods and beverages.[7]

The gradual shift from the use of railroads to trucks for food

transport has made the present system increasingly energy intensive. Trucks use at least three times as much energy per ton mile as
railroads,[8,9] and fuel accounts for approximately 25 percent of
trucks' operating costs.[10] Railroads, on the other hand, spend less
than 8 percent of their operating costs for fuel, but handle only
about 22 percent of all U.S. food shipments.[11, 12]

Part of the reason for the decline in the use of railroads is the
construction of the national Interstate Highway System which helped
to promote the trucking industry at the taxpayer's expense. From
1970 to 1979, the railroads' share of perishable foods shipments
dropped 58 percent.[13] Chronic problems of long delays, inflexi-
bility, financial hardships, and unreliability have plagued railroads
and seriously reduced their ability to compete with trucks. The use of
more flexible trailer-on flat-cars (TOFC) or piggyback rail service
has grown in recent years, however, returning some of the long-
distance produce traffic to railroads.[14]

Except for grains, very little food is shipped by barge. Despite
their relative fuel efficiency, these huge boats are extremely
limited in the number of areas they can serve, since few U.S.
population centers are built around navigable waters. For maximum efficiency, barges must carry large amounts of food, which
makes refrigeration very difficult.

At the present time, there are more than 4 million trucks in this
country used primarily to transport food, enough for every citizen to
have his own truck for one week every year.[15] These 4 million trucks
travel 45 billion miles annually, a distance equal to 242 trips to the
sun![16] Twenty-seven percent of all truck miles[17] and four percent of
the domestic motor fuel supply is used just to transport food.[18] Food
trucks burn up $5.5 billion worth of fuel each year,[19] expel over four
million tons of pollutants into the air,[20] and cause millions of dollars
damage to public highways.

Many of the problems associated with truck transportation
result from the size and weight of modern trucks. The legal gross
vehicle weight in many states is now up to 80,000 pounds.[21]
Although the total state and federal taxes paid by large trucks are
as much as 7 to 8 times that paid by automobiles on a per mile
basis, the General Accounting Office has found that a single fully
loaded 80,000 pound truck does as much damage to a mile of
roadway as 9,600 automobiles.[22] In California, local governments
spend $100 million each year to repair damaged roadbeds, and
99 percent of the damages are due to vehicles weighing more
than 6,000 pounds.[23]

There are other hidden costs of transporting food which are more difficult to measure. Food spoilage and waste during long-distance transportation amount to losses of $300 million annually.[24] When a breakdown in the transportation system occurs, it is quite costly, both to farmers and to consumers. The truckers strike of 1979 caused $1 million in losses to melon-growers in Florida alone.[25]

Many taxpayers bridle at the thought of subsidizing private industries like trucks and railroads. But food transportation subsidies benefit most citizens. If they were ended, the higher costs of moving food would simply be passed on to consumers, raising food prices and hurting poor people. As long as we demand food from all over the world, we will have to pay for transporting it.

Our extensive food transportation system brings us a great variety of fresh foods all year. But this system uses huge quantities of scarce, expensive fuel, and lengthy supply lines can easily be cut by a strike, or a natural disaster, or an energy shortage. Continued dependence on such a system means continual vulnerability for our food supply.

4
Land Use/Soil Abuse

Erosion is a deadly enemy of U.S. farmland. Every year, we lose about 6.4 billion tons of topsoil to erosion,[1] more than enough to cover all the cropland in the New England states of Maine, New Hampshire, Vermont, Massachusetts, Connecticut and Rhode Island, plus New York, New Jersey, Pennsylvania, Delaware, Maryland, Alabama, Arizona, California and Florida with over one inch of dirt, or to bury every supermarket in the United States under 208 feet of earth.[2] The productive equivalent of at least three million acres of farmland is lost every year because of erosion.[3]

In 1977, sheet, rill and wind erosion soil losses from agricultural land came to more than four billion tons. Losses to gully, stream bank, roads and roadsides, and construction sites erosion amounted to about 1.11 billion tons.[4] No figures are collected for erosion caused by snow melt or improper irrigation techniques, but these losses are substantial.

In an average year, more than one-third of all our cropland suffers erosion beyond the "tolerable rate" of about five tons per acre, the maximum rate at which the soil's fertility can be "maintained."[5] Overall, the soil loss per acre of cultivated cropland in the United States averages 5.1 tons annually.[6]

In some areas, this problem is especially acute. Iowa, a prime farming state, loses almost 10 tons of topsoil per acre each year, nearly twice the tolerable rate.[7] For every pound of wheat harvested in eastern Washington, 20 pounds of topsoil are lost.[8] In Texas, wind erosion alone blows 15 tons of topsoil yearly from each acre of cropland.[9] Nationwide, five or six pounds of topsoil are destroyed by erosion in the production of each pound of corn.[10]

At the heaviest rates of erosion, we are destroying an inch of topsoil in 10 to 20 years[11] —topsoil that takes from 100 to 1,500 years to replace, depending on the climate and underlying bedrock.[12] Estimates indicate that we are currently losing 25 percent more soil than during the dust bowl years of the 1930s, despite the fact that we now have *less* land under cultivation.[13] At present rates of soil erosion, some major wheat producing areas of the United States have only one or two decades of productivity left, and after that the land will be suitable only for parking lots for abandoned farm machinery.

Erosion has already taken a heavy toll on our productivity. In the last 200 years, it has destroyed at least one-third of our topsoil. During this time, nearly 236 million acres (370,000 square miles) have been ruined or impoverished for agriculture by erosion.[14] In some parts of the country, the remaining topsoil is only five or six inches deep.[15]

Erosion is also responsible for the slow but steady decline in soil productivity. The soil eroded each year carries with it 12 million tons of nitrogen and 3 million tons of phosphorus, worth $1.6 billion.[16] Estimates are that for every inch of soil lost in the Corn Belt, corn yields are reduced by three bushels per acre.[17]

This loss of productivity has been remedied by the ever-increasing use of synthetic fertilizers and pesticides, but the true costs were masked by a huge subsidy from cheap oil. Now that oil is no longer cheap and this subsidy is removed, the farmer is caught in a bind. He can try to maintain productivity levels with the now high-priced fertilizers and pesticides, or he can cut back and run the risk of drastically reduced yields from his depleted land.

The costs of this soil erosion are as staggering as they are difficult to accurately determine. If we assume an average worth of $1,000 per acre of cropland, with six inches of good topsoil, the loss would amount to more than $6 billion worth of cropland potential each year.[18] If we figure what it would cost to replace this with soil purchased from the local nursery or landscaper (assuming the vast quantities required were available), the total comes to $57 billion annually.[19] This loss is doubly serious because it represents the destruction of an irreplaceable resource, and not just the loss of money.

Added to those figures must be the costs that this soil loss incurs in the form of deteriorated water quality and fish habitat and wetland management. Silt removal from United States waterways and drainage ways costs the United States more than $500 million

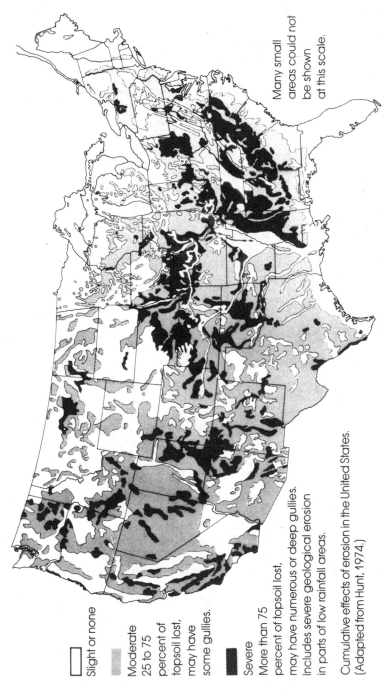

Many small
areas could not
be shown
at this scale.

Slight or none

Moderate
25 to 75
percent of
topsoil lost,
may have
some gullies.

Severe
More than 75
percent of topsoil lost,
may have numerous or deep gullies.
Includes severe geological erosion
in parts of low rainfall areas.

Cumulative effects of erosion in the United States.
(Adapted from Hunt, 1974.)

Source: Paul R. Ehrlich, Anne H. Ehrlich, and John P. Holdren, *Ecoscience: Population, Resources, Environment.* San
Francisco: W.H. Freeman and Company, 1977, p. 258.

per year.[20] Many expensive reservoirs are silting up so rapidly that they will last only half as long as originally intended.[21] The annual loss in capacity is valued at $2.87 billion.[22]

Sediment is the major pollutant—in terms of quantity—entering U.S. lakes, rivers and streams.[23] Sediment clogs waterways and reduces the efficiency of irrigation and drainage systems. Sedimentation can hinder cropland productivity by depositing coarse, infertile soils on top of productive bottomland soils.[24]

Development and Other Abuses

The frightening figures on soil erosion are not the end of the story, however. In addition to the land destroyed by erosion, we are losing cropland each year to salinity, acid rain, suburban sprawl, and other non-agricultural causes, such as building, paving and permanent flooding.[25] Every year 3 million acres of cropland and potential cropland are lost through development.[26] Of this land, about one million acres are prime farmland. This land is invaluable, because it is up to three times more productive than the new marginal land brought into agricultural use as a replacement.[27]

Together, *erosion and development waste about 34 square miles of U.S. agricultural productivity every day.*[28] This daily loss of cropland productivity *alone* could provide a year's minimum diet for 260,000 people.[29] Given the extent of hunger and starvation in the world, this soil loss takes on enormous significance. In addition, the extra food produced from this cropland would be worth about $1.7 billion to American farmers.[30]

Our soil is damaged further by compaction. The use of heavy machinery presses down the soil, making it less absorbent, and plant roots have difficulty taking up deep soil nutrients. As a result, more fertilizer is needed to maintain crop growth. In addition, as the soil gets harder, more energy is needed to plow it.

Continual, heavy use of herbicides and pesticides can destroy the living organisms which make up one to five percent of normal soil.[31] Repeated plowing does the same thing by increasing oxidation losses. The destruction of this organic matter reduces tilth, the ability of the soil to hold water and bind nutrients in forms that will resist leaching but are available to plants. Such "dead" earth is useful only for holding up plants, and any necessary nutrients must be added to the soil.

The search for new and old energy sources also adds to the stress on agricultural land. Growing crops to provide fuel on a commercial scale would require major changes in current agriculture. The USDA estimates that it would take about 300 million acres

Sediment, which is an end product of soil erosion, is by volume the greatest single pollutant in surface waters. It is also the principal carrier of other pollutants such as plant nutrients and chemicals which are attached to soil particles. Sediment levels are affected by natural conditions such as soil characteristics and climate, land use and intensity of use, and erosion control practices.

Algae and rooted plants are appearing in many bodies of water in response to nutrient enrichment from erosion, sewage disposal, and other sources. Too, there is a close pattern between high algae counts (over 10,000), the location of major agricultural areas, and phosphorus and nitrogen levels in streams.

SUSPENDED SEDIMENT CONCENTRATION, MILLIGRAMS PER LITER, 1976*

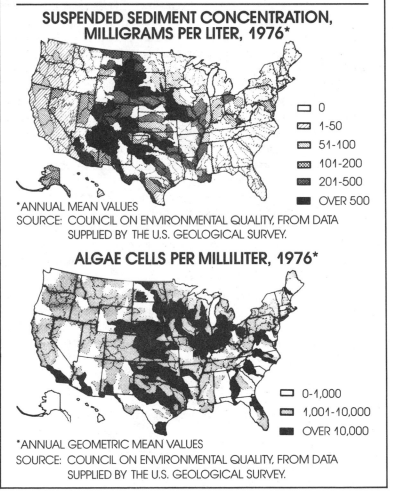

- ☐ 0
- ▨ 1-50
- ▧ 51-100
- ▦ 101-200
- ▩ 201-500
- ■ OVER 500

*ANNUAL MEAN VALUES
SOURCE: COUNCIL ON ENVIRONMENTAL QUALITY, FROM DATA
    SUPPLIED BY THE U.S. GEOLOGICAL SURVEY.

ALGAE CELLS PER MILLILITER, 1976*

- ☐ 0-1,000
- ▦ 1,001-10,000
- ■ OVER 10,000

*ANNUAL GEOMETRIC MEAN VALUES
SOURCE: COUNCIL ON ENVIRONMENTAL QUALITY, FROM DATA
    SUPPLIED BY THE U.S. GEOLOGICAL SURVEY.

Source: 1977 Handbook of Agricultural Charts Agricultural Handbook No.
    524, USDA, p. 28.

of corn to produce just 10 percent of the nation's current energy usage, about three times the acreage presently in corn production and 75 percent of the total cropland in use today.[32] The Office of Technology Assessment has estimated that producing enough gasohol to power most of the cars in the United States would require putting 30 to 70 million additional acres into intensive crop production.[33] That would accelerate erosion problems and contribute to other environmental damages.

Generating and transmitting electricity also require substantial amounts of land. New coal and nuclear power plants may take up 1.5 to 2 million acres of agricultural land.[34] Hydroelectric power plants commonly have reservoirs of 1,000 to 25,000 acres, which often cover valleys classified as prime farmland.[35] Transmission line rights-of-way currently occupy 4 million acres and will require 1.5 to 3 million additional acres by the year 2000.[36]

Surface mining for coal and other minerals had affected 5.7 million acres by 1977.[37] Surface mining currently disturbs an average of 400,000 acres per year, according to the Soil Conservation Service.[38] Although cropland used for surface mining is supposed to be restored to its former condition, there is some doubt that this is possible. Changes in the soil structure and excessive compaction may permanently impair productivity.[39]

Our response to this enormous problem has not been much better in its net effect than that of the ancient Mediterraneans, who bankrupted their once-rich soils into desert.[40] Our programs and policies to stop erosion are grossly inadequate, and some of the limited funds marked for soil conservation have been used for programs to increase crop yields.[41]

In 1937, Franklin Roosevelt remarked that "the nation that destroys its soil destroys itself." Current Agriculture Department Secretary, John R. Block echoed these sentiments in a recent discussion of what will happen if we continue to destroy our farmland: "We won't be talking critical problems; we'll be talking fatalities."[42] American soils are the most productive body of farmland on the face of the earth. But unless we start conserving this land, it will someday be gone, and our future with it.

5
Monoculture

In the spring of 1970, corn fields in Florida were struck with corn leaf blight. As the growing season progressed, the disease spread northward and westward through the corn belt. Many fields were destroyed almost completely.[1] When the epidemic finally ended, it had destroyed about 15 percent of our total corn crop—some 700 million bushels.[2]

Scientists soon discovered that not all corn was susceptible to this blight. Only plants that carried what was known as Texas (T) cytoplasm—cell material from a particular strain of corn—were vulnerable. And for perhaps the first time, the general public became aware of the problems associated with crop mono- culture, the growing of a single variety over a widespread area.

In an uncultivated state, a field or forest contains a great diversity of plants. When pests attack a particular species, the damage seldom spreads far, because the pest soon encounters a different variety. In addition, over the years many of the plants develop natural resistance to their enemies.

When man began to domesticate plants, this natural balance was upset. The goal of a farmer was always to find the best plants he could. Why grow corn that produced only one ear per plant when you could just as easily grow a variety that produced two or three ears? So as time passed, farmers naturally grew more of the better yielding crop varieties and discarded less productive types.

Indeed, the history of agriculture is a story of declining food variety. At least 500 major vegetable varieties were cultivated in ancient times. Today only 20 species are used in field cultivation. Ninety-five percent of our food now comes from no more than 30 plants.[3] Monoculture is a basic fact of modern agriculture.

37

In this century, plant geneticists have been very successful in breeding high-yield plants by combining the best traits of different varieties. In 1915, an average acre of corn yielded 25.9 bushels. In 1979, the average acre yielded 95.1 bushels. For wheat, the yield rose from 13.9 bushels per acre in 1915 to 31.4 bushels in 1979.[4]

To maintain these high crop yields, however, farmers have resorted to extensive use of chemical fertilizers and pesticides, and to increasing reliance on a few select varieties. In the United States today, the amount of genetic uniformity among major crops is frightening. Just two varieties of peas, for example, are planted on 96 percent of our acreage. Six varieties of corn are grown on 71 percent of our acreage.[5] The genetic base of our cultivated crops is so narrow that they are highly vulnerable to a new race of pathogen or a new biotype of insect pest.[6]

While breeding plants for high yields, scientists can also breed in resistance to specific insects and diseases. But many pests are extremely adaptable, and over time they may develop forms that can infect new varieties. The result can be an epidemic such as the corn blight of 1970. Scientists can then develop a variety with resistance to the new pest, but the process usually takes at least five years and sometimes as long as 20 years.[7]

With widespread monoculture, a sort of "pest cycle" often develops. Here's how it works, using the example of wheat rust. "(1) A variety of wheat is developed with good resistance to the locally prevailing races of rust; (2) the variety is grown on a large scale, partly because of its resistance; (3) a race of rust capable of attaching to the host evolves, increases rapidly, and causes an epidemic; (4) a gene for resistance to the new race is isolated and bred into a new variety; (5) the variety is grown on a large scale and the cycle starts over again."[8]

Monoculture has other negative effects on the soil and on farm economics. Continuous row cropping can cause serious erosion, and it requires heavy use of chemical fertilizers and pesticides to maintain good yields. With a single crop, the farmer is more vulnerable. If disease hits, or prices drop, he or she may lose heavily. Weeds tend to adapt and flourish. And identical growing seasons over wide areas make crops more susceptible to drought.[9]

To cope with these problems, plant scientists maintain seed banks, or germplasm collections, where different varieties are stored. Then, when a problem such as corn leaf blight arises, they find a variety with natural resistance and try to breed that characteristic into the next generation. For good results, however, these seed banks must be as diverse as possible, and properly maintained. And there must be sources in the wild for new and different plant varieties.

The U.S. Department of Agriculture maintains a National Seed Storage Laboratory at Fort Collins, Colorado, where more than 1,300 species of seed are stored.[10] But many scientists consider this collection inadequate. The stocks are maintained in cold storage, so they are not available for study and experimentation.[11] And current levels of funding for germplasm maintenance are inadequate for the work that needs to be done.[12]

In addition, natural centers of genetic diversity are disappearing. More wild land is coming under cultivation. Many plants are becoming extinct; estimates run as high as 1,000 species annually.[13] The dependence on monoculture is spreading across the globe. Already, the world's three main cereal crops—wheat, corn (maize), and rice—produce more in terms of dry edible matter than all other crops put together.[14] And with the so-called green revolution, Third World farmers abandoned locally adapted, diverse crops in favor of high-yield, uniform varieties. These varieties have increased food production, but at the same time they are "destroying the genetic variability which makes the success of such programs possible."[15]

There are signs, however, that the revolution may be winding down. Poor farmers are discovering that while their yields might be better, they are having other problems: poor storage life of crops, increased need for expensive fertilizers and pesticides, and required yearly seed purchases.* In many places, they are coming back to proven local varieties.[16]

Sadly, many gardeners are following the lead of farmers. In the past, gardeners often developed strains of vegetables and fruits that were particularly suited to their locality, and passed the seeds on to family and friends. But now, smitten by the desire for new varieties and better harvests, they are switching to a more limited number of high-yield types, and another valuable source of genetic diversity is being lost.

Seed companies also play a role in this trend toward monoculture. Many seed companies have been acquired by large corporations, such as ITT, Union Carbide, Upjohn, and Shell/Olin.[17] Control

---

*High yield varieties are nearly always hybrids, which produce either useless or sterile seeds. So farmers can't save seed to plant another year, they must buy new seed.

over seeds is becoming concentrated in the hands of companies whose primary interests are in such things as chemicals and energy.[18] Already, four companies—Dekalb, Pioneer, Sandoz, and Ciba-Geigy—control about two-thirds of all seed corn sales in the U.S. And these same four companies have 59 percent of the hybrid sorghum market.[19]

These large corporations are now pushing for broader seed patenting laws, arguing that in order to justify the money spent on research they must have exclusive rights to sell particular seeds. But these laws raise some dangerous possibilities. Seeds are the basic source of human food, and exclusive control by one company may infringe on the public right of choice. Seed companies, rather than consumers, may decide what kind of food we will eat, what its quality will be, and how it will be produced.

Additional patent laws would also put further financial pressure on smaller seed companies, who could not compete with their larger, better capitalized rivals in a restricted market. These smaller companies are good sources of unusual varieties, and their loss would accelerate the movement toward genetic uniformity. The President's Commission on World Hunger, as recently as March, 1980, said that food crop vulnerability "has been given a big boost by plant patenting laws."[20]

The recent history of the U.S. Plant Variety Protection Office is not encouraging. Forty-six percent of all the certificates they have issued (as of March, 1979) went to 17 large firms that have acquired once-independent seed companies. Of all the patents issued by that date, 72 percent were for just six crops.[21] Gardeners and farmers are not getting better yields for lower cost, as supporters of such legislation claim.[22]

Monoculture has clearly been a blessing in some ways. Without a certain amount of genetic uniformity, food production around the world would be lower, and hunger and starvation might be more widespread. But monoculture, if not carefully controlled, may turn out to be a bargain with the devil: those high yields come along with a high susceptibility to problems. And if the trend toward monoculture persists, the possibility for disaster increases.

6
Energy

With the exception of the solar energy used as an energy source by plants, the U.S. food system is powered almost entirely by fossil fuels. Because these fuels are becoming scarcer and more costly, and are subject to the vagaries of international political change or blackmail, that dependence is highly dangerous. A sustainable food system cannot be run on nonsustainable fuels.

Domestic consumption of oil and natural gas has risen dramatically in recent years (see figures 1, 2, and 3), and these fuels could soon be priced beyond most people's ability to pay for them. At our current rates of consumption, proven U.S. oil and gas reserves would not carry up very far into the next century.[1] The United States currently imports about 40 percent of its fuel.[2]

The U.S. food system does very poorly in terms of energy-use-per-food-calorie output. It takes more energy to produce a calorie of food in the United States than it does almost anywhere else. On the average, our system burns 6.4 units of commercial energy for each unit of food energy that reaches our plates.[3] Some foods take considerably more; processed vegetables, for example, consume nearly 16 units of energy for every unit of food energy produced.[4] To feed the world with a U.S.-type food system would take up to 60 percent of the total amount of commercial energy in use globally,[5] and such a system would burn up all of Earth's known petroleum reserves in 13 years.[6]

The U.S. food system consumes about 16.5 percent of the total energy used in the country (see figure 4), and this energy cost consumers more than $36 billion in 1975.[7] Over 50 percent of the food system energy comes from oil, and at least a quarter of this

41

amount is imported oil.[8] And although only three percent of
total U.S. energy consumption is devoted to agricultural production,[9] a huge share of this energy—93 percent—is derived from
petroleum.[10]

FIGURE 1

YEARLY PETROLEUM CONSUMPTION, U.S.

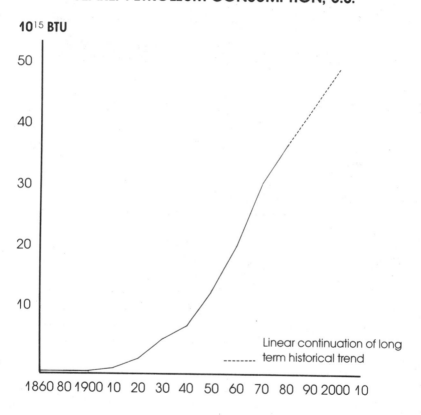

10^{15} **BTU**

Linear continuation of long
-------- term historical trend

1860 80 1900 10 20 30 40 50 60 70 80 90 2000 10

Sources: U.S., Department of Commerce, Bureau of the Census, *Historical
Statistics of the United States, Colonial Times to 1970*, Part 1,
p. 588. Washington, D.C.: U.S., Government Printing Office.

Congressional Research Service, *Energy Information Digest,
Basic Data on Energy Resources, Reserves, Production,
Consumption, and Prices,* July 1977, p. 34. Washington, D.C.,
Government Printing Office.

1980 data from National Energy Information Center.

FIGURE 2

YEARLY NATURAL GAS CONSUMPTION, U.S.

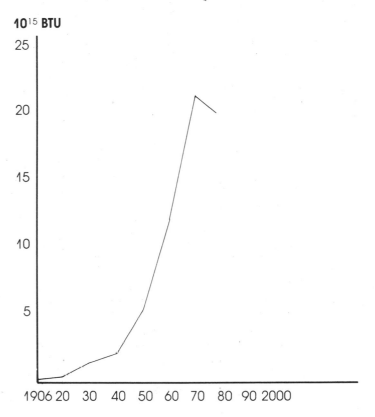

10¹⁵ BTU

Sources: U.S., Department of Commerce, Bureau of the Census, *Historical Statistics of the United States, Colonial Times to 1970,* Part 1, p. 595. Washington, D.C.: U.S. Government Printing Office.

Congressional Research Service, *Energy Information Digest, Basic Data on Energy Resources, Reserves, Production, Consumption, and Prices,* July 1977, p. 33. Washington, D.C.: U.S. Government Printing Office.

U.S., Department of Energy, *Monthly Energy Review,* September 1981, Energy Information Administration, p. 52.

FIGURE 3

COST OF OIL AND NATURAL GAS

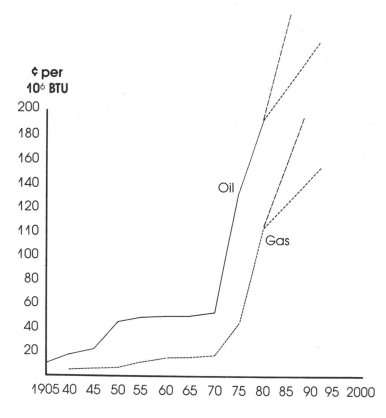

          ------ Long term linear continuation
                  of historical trend

          ____ Short term linear continuation
                  of historical trend

Sources: U.S., Department of Commerce, Bureau of the Census, *Statistical Abstract of the United States 1980*, p. 607. Washington, D.C., Government Printing Office.

          U.S., Department of Commerce, Bureau of the Census, *Historical Statistics of the United States, Colonial Times to 1970*, Part 1, pp. 593-5. Washington, D.C.: U.S. Government Printing Office.

FIGURE 4

MAJOR CATEGORIES OF ENERGY USE IN THE U.S. THE SHADED PORTION REPRESENTS ENERGY CONSUMPTION BY THE U.S. FOOD SYSTEM.

Federal Energy Administration, 1975

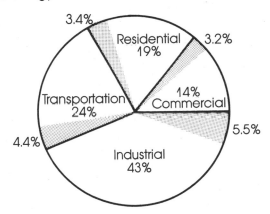

Source: *Energy and You*, Special Circular 246, The Pennsylvania State University, College of Agriculture Extension Service, University Park, Pennsylvania.

ENERGY USED IN THE U.S. FOOD SYSTEM

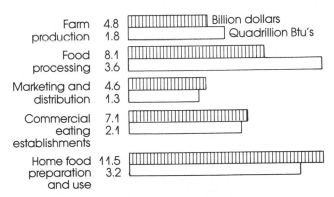

1976 data for farm production. 1975 data for all other categories.
1979 *Handbook of Agricultural Charts.* Agricultural Handbook 561, USDA.

Source: *Cutting Energy Costs* The 1980 Yearbook of Agriculture, U.S. Government Printing Office, 1980, p. 11.

Farming uses more petroleum than any other single industry. General crop farms use over $4.00 worth of petroleum products per acre, while U.S. vegetable farms use over $12.00 worth per acre.[11] By making the United States' "supply of food—its single most critical need—dependent on the continued smooth functioning of a complex distribution system that is vulnerable to energy related disruption"[11] the entire system is endangered.

The potential for trouble is illustrated by a recent Department of Energy study, which found that an energy shortage or reduction of 10 percent would lead to an increase of 55 percent in raw commodity prices.[12] If this reduction were applied to all areas of food production and marketing as well, increases in retail food prices would be even greater.[13] Similarly, slight oil cutbacks or interruption of supplies at a crucial time in the agricultural cycle, such as planting or harvesting, could have a devastating impact on food production capacity.

Despite this vulnerability, the total amount of energy being used by the U.S. food system is increasing at an alarming rate (see figures 5, 6). If this trend continues, the food system will soon outstrip the energy system's ability to supply it. Further, as the food system uses more energy, less is available for the rest of the economy, and the more inflated our food costs become.

This increasing energy use is primarily off the farm, and much of it goes for processing and long-distance transport of food. At the present time, the processing and packaging of food in this country use as much energy as all the farms that produce our food. And for every $2 we spend on energy to grow food, we spend another $1 moving it around.[14]

Each year, shipping fresh produce around the United States uses about 475 million gallons of fuel.[15] In August, 1981, it cost $1.12 for every mile that a large truck moved fruits and vegetables—up almost 11 percent since August, 1980.[16] A truckload of broccoli pulling into New York City from California, for example, would cost $2,000 more than the same truckload coming from nearby New Jersey.[17]

Moving food around not only costs money, it raises the specter of food shortages. In recent testimony before Congress, a spokesman for the Food Marketing Institute urged that food distributors be given the same fuel priority during an energy crisis that farmers have. The spokesman reported that during the 1979 fuel shortage, some distributors "came within a day or two of not having enough fuel to deliver food. In other words, we were only days away from shortages on the shelves of grocery stores around the nation."[18]

FIGURE 5

ENERGY USED IN PRODUCTION AGRICULTURE.

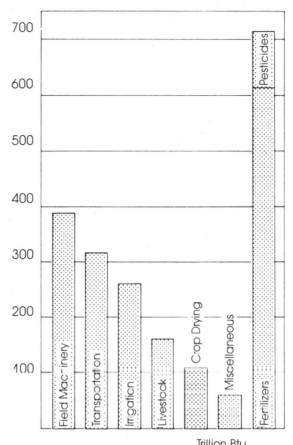

	Trillion Btu	
Field Machinery	391	30%
Till, plant, cultivate, applications, harvest		
Transportation	317	25%
Pickups, on-farm hauling, business auto trips		
Irrigation	261	20%
Livestock, Dairy, Poultry	161	12%
Crop Drying	107	8%
Miscellaneous	61	5%
Total Fuel and Electricity	1,298	100%
Indirect Energy: manufacture of fertilizers and pesticides	716	
Total	2,014	

Source: *Energy and You,* Special Circular 246, The Pennsylvania State University, College of Agriculture Extension Service, University Park, Pennsylvania.

Synthetic fuels, derived from coal and shale, are sometimes put forward as an alternative to petroleum. But under present economic conditions, these fuels cost 2 to 4 times as much as naturally occurring liquid fuels.[19] Oil shale processing is also very costly in terms of resources, using approximately 39 gallons of water per barrel of shale oil. (All the oil shale deposits are located in the water-short states of Colorado, Utah and Wyoming.[20]) And finally, both shale and coal technologies result in huge amounts of potentially destructive and hazardous chemical wastes.

The energy on which the U.S. food system depends is caught in a frightening cycle. Prices are rising, demand is increasing, the supply is decreasing, and our suppliers are unreliable. Until we lessen our reliance on non-renewable energy sources, the food supply for much of the country will be dangerously vulnerable.

FIGURE 6

TOTAL U.S. FOOD SYSTEM ENERGY USE COMPARED TO ON-FARM AGRICULTURAL ENERGY USE.

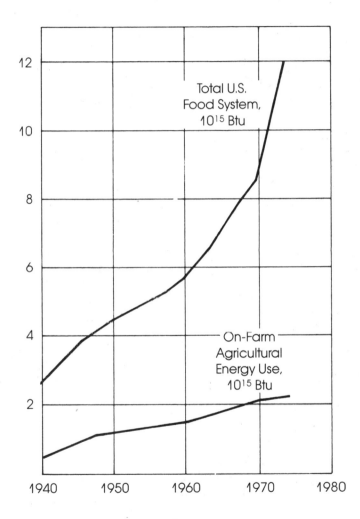

Source: *Energy and You*, Special Circular 246, The Pennsylvania State University, College of Agriculture Extension Service, University Park, Pennsylvania.

7
Mineral Base

Conventional farming in the United States is almost totally depedent on chemical fertilizers, particularly those that supply the three essential plant nutrients—phosphorus, nitrogen and potassium. About 96 percent of the corn, 62 percent of the wheat, 77 percent of the cotton, 31 percent of the soybeans and nearly 100 percent of the vegetables produced in this country are fertilized.[1]

In 1980, U.S. farmers used 5.39 million tons of phosphorus, 11.4 million tons of nitrogen, and 6.16 million tons of potassium.[2] We now apply an average of 111 pounds of synthetic fertilizer nutrients per acre of cropland each year, which amounts to 210 pounds for every person in the country.[3] Without this fertilizer, yields would drop an estimated 50 percent.[4]

But there are supply problems with each of these minerals. Phosphate imports for 1979-1980 were up 23 percent over the 1977-1978 level, while imports of anhydrous ammonia (nitrogen fertilizer) jumped 76 percent in the same period. Only 24 percent of our net supply of potash (potassium fertilizer) for 1979-1980 was from domestic sources.[5]

Phosphorus is particularly vulnerable. The United States is currently the world's leading producer of phosphate rock,[6] the only commercial source of phosphorus. In 1977-1978, the U.S. produced 25 percent of the world's phosphate fertilizer.[7] Our richest deposits are in the Bone Valley of central Florida, and these deposits account for about 75 percent of U.S. production.[8]

Phosphate use has doubled since 1960.[9] The increasing demand for this fertilizer has put a severe strain on our limited resources. U.S. production of phosphate rock is expected to peak about 1985, and to decline over the next two decades. Shortly after

PHOSPHATE CONSUMPTION

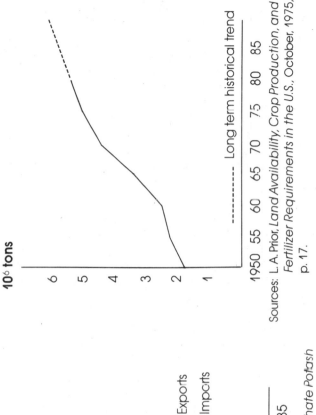

10⁶ tons

---------- Long term historical trend

1950 55 60 65 70 75 80 85

Sources: L. A. Prior, Land Availability, Crop Production, and Fertilizer Requirements in the U.S., October, 1975, p. 17.

U.S., Department of Agriculture, Agricultural Statistics 1980, United States Government Printing Office, Washington, D.C., p. 467.

PHOSPHATE IMPORTS AND EXPORTS

10³ tons

---- Exports

—— Imports

1950 55 60 65 70 75 80 85

Source: The Fertilizer Supply, Nitrogen Phosphate Potash 1979-80, USDA, Agricultural Stabilization and Conservation Service, Washington, D.C., April 1980, p. 16.

the year 2000, our commercially accessible reserves may be exhausted.[10] When our own deposits are gone, we will have to obtain phosphorus from abroad.

Despite our rapidly dwindling stores, the United States is still one of the world's leading *exporters* of phosphate rock. In 1980-81, 42 percent of our production was sold overseas.[11] And recently, a major U.S. producer signed a deal to send the Soviet Union 2.8 million metric tons of phosphate per year for 20 years.[12]

The results of this situation—a rapidly depleting phosphate supply, increasing demand, substantial exports—could be disastrous. Given current trends, by the end of this century, the United States will almost certainly be dependent upon other countries for phosphate rock.

> It seems entirely possible that by 1990 Morocco and various Middle Eastern countries (Jordan, Egypt, Saudi Arabia) will supply 75 percent of the world trade in phosphate rock. If this were to happen, a cartel could easily be formed to control phosphate prices.[13]

Such an action would put us in the same position with phosphate rock as we are in with oil: unable to survive without massive imports, and forced to pay whatever price the cartel asks.

Nitrogen presents another problem. There is no danger that we will run out of nitrogen; it makes up about 78 percent of our air. Most plants cannot use nitrogen in this "free" form, however. To be available to them it must be "fixed," or combined with another element. The most common way to fix nitrogen for fertilizer is to combine it with hydrogen to make ammonia. And the most widely used source of hydrogen is natural gas—which is in short supply and getting more and more expensive.

Natural gas is used almost exclusively in the production of ammonia because it is a relatively clean, low-carbon fuel. To make one ton of ammonia requires about 38,000 cubic feet of natural gas,[14] enough to heat the average U.S. house for nearly four months.[15] The manufacture of ammonia fertilizer uses about two percent of U.S. production and five percent of world production of natural gas,[16] and chemical fertilizer represents the single largest energy drain on the U.S. farming system.[17] (See Figure 5 in Energy Chapter.) More energy is used to produce synthetic fertilizer than is used in tilling, planting, cultivating, and harvesting all the crops in the United States.[18]

U.S. NITROGEN FERTILIZER CONSUMPTION
PRIMARY NUTRIENT CONTENT

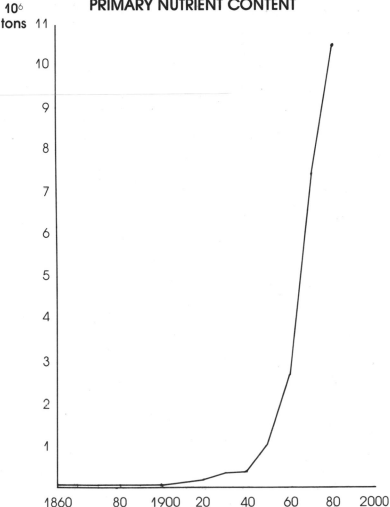

Sources: U.S., Department of Agriculture, *Consumption of Commercial Fertilizers, Primary Plant Nutrients, and Micronutrients,* Statistical Reporting Service, Crop Reporting Board, Statistical Bulletin #472, Washington, D.C., Government Printing Office, 1966, pp. 2, 3.

U.S., Department of Agriculture, Commercial Fertilizers *Consumption by Class of Year Ended June 30, 1979,* Crop Reporting Board, Economics, Statistics and Cooperative Service, December 1979, p. 14.

UNITED STATES IMPORTS OF NITROGEN FERTILIZER

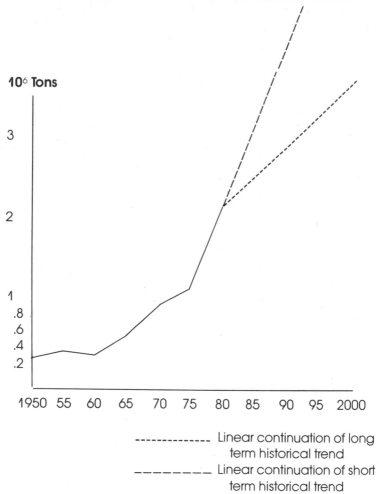

Source: U.S., Department of Agriculture, *The Fertilizer Supply: Nitrogen, Phosphate, Potash 1979-80,* April, 1980, p. 16. Agricultural Stabilization and Conservation Service, Washington, D.C.

While we won't run out of nitrogen, we are running out of natural gas. And when our gas supplies are exhausted, we will either have to import ammonia or make it with other, even more expensive methods: synthetic gas produced from coal[19] or hydrogen produced by the electrolysis of water. The cost of ammonia has already risen rapidly along with natural gas prices, and this rise has led to increased imports of ammonia from countries with cheap, accessible supplies of gas. After nine years of self-sufficiency, the United States became a net importer of ammonia in 1974, and since then imports have approximately equalled exports.[20] In 1979-80, the United States imported about 19 percent of its nitrogen fertilizer, at a cost of over $470 million.[21]

Potassium, the third critical fertilizer element, is made primarily from potash, or potassium oxide. Primary U.S. deposits are in New Mexico, Utah and California, while the largest world reserves are in the Soviet Union and Canada, particularly Saskatchewan. Until 1962, the United States supplied all its own potash needs. In 1979-1980, we produced less than one quarter of the amount we used;[41] nearly 76 percent came from Canada.[22] Potash imports cost the United States $399 million in 1978.[23]

Projections are that the U.S. consumption of potash will double by the year 2000, at which time we will produce less than 10 percent of our total needs.[24] This means we will once again be completely dependent on another country—albeit a friendly one—for an essential element.

Processing potash also has undesirable aspects. It is highly energy intensive—nearly 1,500 kwh of electricity are required to make each ton of potassium fertilizer.[25] The mineral by-products of the process are water soluble, and can cause contamination, while the dust is an air pollutant and has shown negative effects on vegetation surrounding manufacturing plants.[26]

The continued well-being of the U.S. food system depends on the availability of phosphorus, nitrogen and potassium. Yet the future sources of these vital minerals pose serious difficulties for the United States. Without an abundant, reasonably-priced supply, our productivity will be drastically reduced.

8
Environmental Impacts

The increasing use of herbicides, pesticides, and chemical fertilizers has led to the contamination of our soil and water, the destruction of wildlife and increased health problems for farm workers. America's farmers currently use about two pounds of pesticide[1] and 111 pounds of synthetic fertilizer nutrients per acre of cropland.[2]

The use of chemical fertilizers and pesticides is an integral part of conventional farming. These substances are applied before planting to "give crops a good start"; they are applied during the growing season to "ensure high yields"; they are applied after the harvest to "preserve quality during storage and shipping".

Because some of the compounds in these chemicals are novel to the biosphere, they are metabolized slowly or not at all, and tend to accumulate and to concentrate up the food chain. Nearly everyone in the United States consumes small amounts of pesticides daily in food and water, and the average person has a pesticide residue in the fatty tissue of six parts per million. About half of all U.S. food tested contains detectable levels of pesticides.[3]

Chemical fertilizers and pesticides pollute water in three ways: they wash off crops and fields into surface water; they seep into groundwater; and they are blown into streams, rivers, and lakes. These chemicals not only taint our drinking water, they harm fish, waterfowl, and other wildlife.

Air quality is also threatened by agricultural chemicals. Pesticides carried by the wind can harm crops and useful insect populations many miles from their points of application. Fluoride emissions from the phosphate fertilizer industry injure plants and contribute to chronic fluorosis in cattle.[4] Nitrogen fertilizers are suspected of releasing a catalytic form of nitrous oxide that may contribute to the depletion of the ozone layer.[5]

As a final insult, these chemicals—especially pesticides—endanger human health. The United Nations estimates that half a million people throughout the world are poisoned by pesticides every year,[6] about 45,000 of them in the United States.[7] Farmers, despite being able to work in the fresh air and eat plenty of homegrown foods, have been shown to be at higher risk than others of contracting diseases of the respiratory and central nervous systems.[8] Pesticides have been linked to such problems as blood dyscrasias, allergy sensitivities, neurological alterations, hypertension, high blood cholesterol, cardiovascular disease and liver disease. In developing countries, a resurgence of malaria has been attributed to the intensive agricultural practices of the green revolution, which have led to a pesticide resistant mosquito.[9]

The indirect cost of agricultural chemicals is substantial. One study suggested a figure of more than $839 million: $184 million for human health; $12 million for livestock and product losses; $287 million for increased pest resistance and harm to natural pest enemies; $135 million for bee poisonings and reduced pollination; $70 million for crop and tree losses; $11 million for fish and wildlife losses; and $140 million for state and federal pesticide pollution control.[10] And this does not include such things as damage to soil, long-term health effects, and the costs of cleaning up toxic pesticide dumps.

In light of these problems, it is ironic that pesticides are not doing their job very well. In the past 15 years, pesticide use has increased 140 percent.[11] During the same period, however, crop loss to insects increased over 40 percent.[12]

The problem is that pests can develop a resistance to chemicals, which leads to the use of more and/or stronger pesticides. The cycle then repeats itself until we reach the absurd point where we are today: despite massive use of pesticides, crop losses continue to increase. To poison pests, we are slowly poisoning ourselves and our environment. Unless we can break this nonsustainable pattern, the environment may soon be unable to support the continued production of food.

9
Water

A regular supply of water is essential for the survival of plants, animals, and people. Although less than one percent of the world's total supply of water is fresh and available for use, this should be more than enough to meet our needs.[1] Rain and melting snow provide an average of 3,000 gallons a day for every man, woman, and child in the United States.[2] As individuals, we each require less than a gallon a day to meet our essential biological needs. But our other needs place additional demands on this water, and we waste large amounts.

One of the problems is distribution. Water, like food, is not always located where it is needed. Some areas of the U.S. are facing serious water shortages, and highly productive cropland is already being lost. Other areas are threatened with water quality problems, such as salinity and organic pollutants. But so far, little has been done to deal with these growing problems.

Irrigation

The Western United States receives about 27 percent of our annual rainfall, yet it consumes* 84 percent of our national water total. Westerners, per capita, use 14.7 times as much water as people in the East.[3] The primary reason is irrigation, which takes 81

---

*Water usage is measured in two ways: water withdrawn and water consumed. Withdrawals are usages that return a considerable portion of the water to streams, rivers, or ground water sources where it is available for re-use. Consumption represents water that is primarily incorporated into a process or product and is not reused.

percent of all the water consumed in this country.[4] There is much fertile land in the West, but low rainfall, so irrigation is essential for most types of farming. Originally, the surface water used for irrigation was free, and users got water rights for as long as the water was used beneficially.

Today, only about 15 percent of the cultivated cropland in the U.S. is irrigated. But these 55 million acres are vital to our food system: they produce more than 25 percent of the total value of U.S. crops. And the great majority of this irrigated land—83 percent—is in the West.[5]

IRRIGATED LAND IN U.S. (1,000 ACRES)

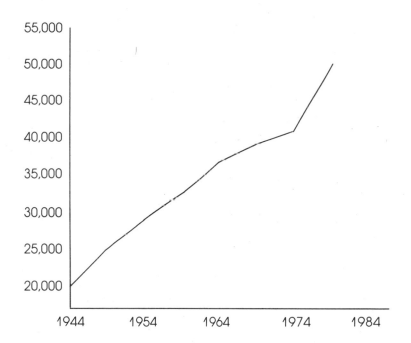

Sources: U.S., Department of Agriculture, *Agricultural Statistics 1980*, (Washington, D.C.: Government Printing Office, 1980), p. 421.

U.S., Department of Commerce, *1978 Census of Agriculture*, Vol. 1, Summary and State Data, Part 51, United States, Bureau of the Census July, 1981, p. 9. Washington, D.C.: U.S. Government Printing Office.

USE OF GROUNDWATER IN IRRIGATION
(BILLION GALLONS DAILY)*

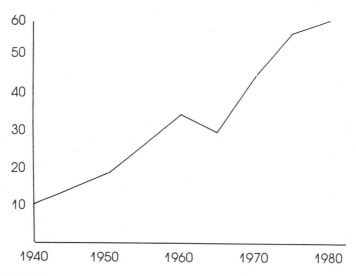

*1940-1960 not strictly comparable to later years due to differences in estimation procedures

Source: U.S., Department of Commerce, *Statistical Abstract of the United States 1980,* Bureau of the Census, (Washington, D.C.: Government Printing Office, 1980), p. 213.

While irrigation is necessary in many areas, it is extremely wasteful. With current practices, less than half the water delivered for irrigation is consumed by crops.[6] The rest is lost to such things as seepage, evaporation, or overwatering. Water-conserving methods of irrigation have been developed and are used in other countries, but these methods have not been widely adopted here.

Initially, only surface water was used for irrigation. But in the 1930's, new pumping methods and cheap energy made it possible to use groundwater. At first this was used primarily as a supplement in dry years, but as irrigated land increased, it became an essential water source. Groundwater irrigation rose from about 11 million acre-feet* in 1945 to over 56 million acre-feet in 1975.[7]

---

*An acre-foot is the measurement used for irrigation water, and equals 12 inches of rain over an acre of ground. One acre-foot amounts to 43,560 cubic feet of water, more than 325,851 gallons or almost 1,358 tons.

Current estimates are that more than half the irrigation water now comes from groundwater sources.[8]

Most of the groundwater in the U.S. has accumulated over centuries in huge underground reservoirs called aquifers. While this water is theoretically replaceable, the spread of irrigation has meant that in many areas groundwater is being used at a rate exceeding replenishable levels. This "mining" of groundwater has now reached major proportions—an estimated 25 percent of our groundwater use is overdrafts.[9] In an average year, 21 billion gallons of water are mined from our groundwater every day.[10]

These large overdrafts of groundwater for irrigation will not, in the short term, deplete our supplies totally. But as water tables fall, and energy prices rise, it becomes more and more expensive to pump groundwater for irrigation. At some point, it costs too much to farm economically, and the land is abandoned.

The worst problems are in the high plains region of Texas, Oklahoma, New Mexico, and Kansas, and in Arizona—areas that contain 20 percent of the West's irrigated land[11] and produced agricultural products worth more than $17 billion in 1978.[11a] Fields here are watered almost exclusively with groundwater. In an average year, less than one-quarter of the groundwater that is used is replaced in five subregions of the Arkansas, Texas and Colorado areas.[12] Sometime in the next 30 years, water withdrawals in these areas will become impractical,[13] and there is no other source of water currently available.

This has already happened in scattered areas. Since 1960, Pinal County, Arizona, has lost nearly 100,000 acres of farmland—more than one-third of the irrigated land in the area.[14] Ten years ago, the area around Pecos, Texas was prime cotton land, with 15 gins and a thousand farmers. In 1973, a leap in natural gas prices made water pumping too expensive, and most of these fields now grow only tumbleweeds.[15] In the next two decades, many other areas can expect similar cropland losses.

Excessive mining of groundwater can also cause subsidence, or sinking of the land surface. As water tables are lowered, the ground compacts and sinks. According to the U.S. Geological Survey, significant subsidence has occurred in Louisiana, Texas, Arizona, New Mexico, and California.[16] In California's San Joaquin Valley, where farmers mine nearly 1.5 million acre-feet (489 billion gallons) of groundwater yearly,[17] the land has sunk as much as 29 feet over the last 50 years.[18] In Central Arizona, subsidence as much as seven feet has occurred since irrigation began.[19]

Overuse of groundwater has other environmental consequences. By reducing the base flow of streams and springs, it has adverse affects on fish and wildlife habitats, especially during dry periods.[20] In coastal regions, it leads to the underground intrusion of salt water.

Some areas of the West are also facing shortages of surface waters, despite intensive management of rivers and lakes. The Colorado River is a prime example. It rises in the Rockies, and passes through seven Western states and part of Mexico before emptying into the Gulf of California. Use of its water was the subject of the longest oral argument in the history of the U.S. Supreme Court, and the 1963 ruling that finally settled the dispute allocated more water than flows in the Colorado.

So far this has not been a problem, since all the states haven't drawn their full share. But the crunch may come in 1985, when the $1.7 billion Central Arizona project will be completed, and divert 390 billion gallons yearly to the Phoenix and Tucson areas.[21] California currently uses more than its share, drawing on Arizona's unused portion. Much of that water travels by canal to the Imperial Valley, irrigating over three million acres of fruit and vegetables worth $1 billion annually.[22] When Arizona starts to use all its water allocation, California will either have to pipe water from the northern part of the state or face the loss of these lucrative croplands.

Irrigation also causes water quality problems, particularly salinity. All waters carry salts, and when irrigation water evaporates, the salts condense and collect in the soil. If the salt content gets too high, it can stunt the growth of plants.

Where soil has good drainage, the salts wash away. But they are either washed into surface or groundwater sources, raising the salt levels there. Already every Western river basin (except the Columbia River Basin) has a high salt level that is rising regularly.[23] An estimated 25 to 35 percent of irrigated land in the West has some kind of salinity problem[24] Annual damages from salinity in the Colorado River are expected to range from $75 to $104 million in 1980 and up to $160 million per year in 2000 if nothing is done to correct this situation.[25]

If the land does not have good drainage, continued irrigation raises groundwater levels. The ground becomes waterlogged, and as the water evaporates from the surface it leaves salt residues behind. Over a period of time, this diminishes and then destroys the soil's usefulness. In the San Joaquin Valley, farms are being hurt by salt build-up from irrigation. On some croplands, yields are down 10 to 35 percent, resulting in income losses of at least $32 million yearly.[26] This process has ruined five million acres of rich farmland on the floodplain of the Indus River in Pakistan.[27]

Finally, there is the problem of water pollution from the run-off of chemical fertilizers, pesticides, and insecticides. (See "Environmental Impacts.") The environmental impact of these substances costs an estimated $839 million annually.[28]

In the years ahead, the demand for water by industry, energy producers, and residential users will increase rapidly, and these groups will compete fiercely with agricultural interests for available water. Meanwhile, federal and state water laws and policies are generally ill-designed and uncoordinated, and conservation programs are seriously inadequate.*

Drinking Water

For the last 50 years or so, Americans have taken it for granted that when they turned on the tap, pure water would flow out. But those days are gone. Much of the water we drink is seriously polluted, even in the water-rich East.

The primary reason for our growing water pollution problem is the rapid increase in the production of waste. The Environmental Protection Agency estimates that we now generate 77 billion pounds of hazardous chemical wastes yearly (350 pounds for each person), and only 10 percent are processed safely.[29] Despite federal grants of nearly $19 billion over the last 10 years for waste-water treatment plants, two-thirds of all U.S. cities still dump partially treated sewage into nearby waters every day.[30] In addition, pollution from runoff of agricultural lands affects 68 percent of the river basins in the United States.[31]

There are several different types of water pollutants. Among the most common are microbiological contaminants—bacteria, viruses, parasites—which are usually treated with chlorine. Other pollutants include various solids suspended in water, such as clay, oil, or mineral fibers, and inorganic solutes, which are primarily trace minerals. Some of these are harmless or even beneficial. Others, such as lead, are highly toxic.

The most widespread and serious pollutants are organic chemicals. These come from several sources: run-off from farms and cities, waste from industrial plants; and effluents from sewage treat-

---

*See Michael Baram, *In Order to Have Water*, report to the U.S. Department of the Interior, Bracken and Baram, Boston, Massachusetts, 1980.

ment facilities. Many of these chemicals are known to be danger-ous, but we are just now beginning to understand the harmful effects they may have.

The best-known example of chemical poisoning comes from the Love Canal, near Buffalo, New York, where a landfill containing 82 chemical compounds polluted the drinking water of a nearby housing development.[32] Residents fear that high incidences of cancer, birth defects, and respiratory and neurological disorders will result.[33] More than half of the families have now been moved with federal help.

Another typical example comes from Iowa, where a pharma-ceutical company dumped chemicals into the Cedar River water-shed, the source of drinking water for much of North-Central Iowa. One of the more dangerous chemicals has been found 65 miles downriver in the wells supplying Waterloo. Some scientists believe this pollution is directly linked to the fact that residents of both Waterloo and Charles City have elevated levels of bladder cancer.[34]

Pollution control efforts, while fairly extensive, have been less than adequate. One problem is that tests for many contaminants, especially organic chemicals, are complicated and costly. Another is that most activities to date have focused on "point source" pollution—contamination which comes from a specific, identifi-able spot such as an industrial plant or a sewage treatment facility. With this type of pollution, it is usually possible to identify the source and limit the damage. But at least half of the pollutants come from wider areas called "nonpoint" sources, and enter water in a dif-fused and diluted form. The major sources of nonpoint pollution are agricultural activities, road salting, city stormwater and street run-off.[35]

Over the past 10 years, the federal government has spent about $43 billion to control point source pollution,[36] and some progress has been made. But current funds allocated for the control of nonpoint sources total only $232 million.[37] And despite past expenditures, the states estimate that they need $100 billion to construct municipal wastewater treatment facilities adequate for their projected 1990 populations.[38] The Council on Environmental Quality suggests that to meet all current water pollution abatement laws will require spending $248 billion over the next decade.[39]

Pollution of surface water is not a recent problem. Even before toxic industrial and municipal wastes were dumped into our rivers and streams, they often received rotting leaves, animal and human wastes, and other natural debris. The big difference was that these natural products were usually part of the food chain, and rarely exceeded the stream's ability to clean itself. Today we contribute so much pollution that our waterways cannot clean themselves, and the problem has spread from our surface waters to a more serious location: our groundwaters.

More than half of Americans now get their drinking water from groundwater.[40] Once groundwater is polluted, it is extremely difficult to clean up, and the process may take decades. The reason is that groundwater does not have the natural cycle of purification that surface water does; there is no sunshine to evaporate it and remove salt and other pollutants. In addition, it flows so slowly that it cannot clean itself as it moves through the earth.[41]

Groundwater pollution is a slow but steady process. When water comes in contact with chemical wastes, it removes the soluble parts, forming a highly polluted liquid called leachate. The more water that contacts the waste, or the more liquid the waste, the more leachate is formed. This leachate can then enter surface waters or seep into groundwater.

The EPA has located more than 180,000 chemical waste disposal sites around the country. In a spot study of 8,200 of these sites, the agency found that 72 percent were nothing more than unlined holes in the ground, and 700 of these were within a mile of wells that used groundwater.[42] Reported cases of groundwater pollution are increasing: 44 in Massachusetts, 25 in Pennsylvania, more than 200 in California,[43] about 300 in Michigan.[44]

In addition to these dangers, we are now learning, ironically, that a primary method of purifying water may itself be causing pollution. Traditionally, microbiological contaminants have been controlled with chlorine. But researchers have discovered that in the purification process, chlorine interacts with the water and forms synthetic chemicals. Chloroform—a known carcinogen—is the most common, and a recent EPA survey of chlorine-treated water showed chloroform in over 95 percent of the finished samples.[45] A Columbia University study found that women who drank chlorinated water had 44 percent more risk of dying from cancer of the urinary or gastrointestinal tract than women who drink unchlorinated water.[46] Chlorinated water has also been linked to high blood pressure and anemia.

Pure water can still be found. But unless we are willing to pay the price to control the production and disposal of dangerous wastes, and practice conservation, good drinking water will become scarcer.

10
Climate

The weather is the most capricious variable in our food production system. The sun supplies most of the energy needed to grow crops, but if it shines too much, they wither and die. Rain provides the moisture plants need for life, but floods or hail can cause widespread destruction. Since the beginning of agriculture, man has been both blessed and cursed by the climate.

Modern technology has overcome many of the problems of farming, and even moderated the effects of bad weather. During a drought, for example, some farmers can irrigate their crops. Dams and drainage canals can limit flood damage. But these things have only limited success; our best efforts are no match for nature. As a result, scientists have focused primarily on trying to predict the weather, and then take steps to minimize any negative effect on our food supply.

Most people consider good weather to be "normal," while bad weather is abnormal. But what is normal with weather is variability.[1] In the past, people coped with hard times as best they could, and hoped to survive until better days came. The margin for error, however, is thinner now than ever. World population is at record levels and growing. Millions of people exist on minimal food and water, and a climate change that affects these could spell disaster.[2]

Only a few scientists are predicting that a sudden, major climate change, such as a new ice age, is likely in the near future.[3] Many suggest, however, that over the next 50 to 100 years there will be significant changes, with a profound impact on world food supplies.[4] Yet the primary concern is not with these long-term trends, which allow some time for adjustment, but with short-term changes that catch us largely by surprise.[5]

History does give us reason to worry about the weather. The past 60 to 70 years have been the warmest in the last millennium,[6] and agriculture as we know it has developed during this favorable time. But a recent CIA report warned that the world may be returning to the climate that existed for the 400 years prior to 1850, "an era of drought, famine, and political unrest in the Western world."[7]

Last year, parts of the U.S. suffered from drought, and the peanut crop was down 42 percent, while corn yields dropped 16 percent.[8] But when compared to the past, this was a very minor drought. Paleo-climatic reconstruction indicates that a drought lasting about 200 *years* afflicted the region of the state of Iowa beginning about 900 A.D.[9] There was a great drought over much of the country from 1276 to 1313, and it is difficult to comprehend the devastation that would result if such an event recurred. A lengthy drought hit the Midwest from 1884 to 1895, and between 1888 and 1892 half the settlers in Kansas and Nebraska left for greener fields.[10] And finally, the dry years of the 1930's ruined many farms and farmers.

Some forecasters see major droughts ahead. Dr. Douglas A. Paine, an atmospheric scientist at Cornell University, predicts that most of the country will experience a serious drought in 1982 and 1983, with a more limited drought lasting until 1986.[11] While many others dispute his findings, Paine gained some credibility by correctly predicting a wet spring in 1981.

Left to its own devices, the Earth does follow some general cycles. Right now, for example, we should be heading (very slowly) toward a new ice age. The inter-glacial period we have known during recorded history ought to be ending in the next 5,000 to 10,000 years.[12]

But things are not that simple, because many different factors have a significant impact on the weather. Some are natural, such as solar activity, planetary tides, and changes in the Earth's orbit and rotation. Others are man-related: the increase in atmospheric carbon dioxide (CO_2), the deterioration of the ozone layer, particles in the air, and heat generated by energy use.[13] And these factors interact in ways that make prediction extremely difficult.

Indeed, while most of us see little variation in overall weather patterns, it is important to realize that slight changes can have a significant effect on agriculture. A drop of 2°C. below the optimum temperatures of the 1940's would cut the growing season in much of the Midwest by 20 to 30 days.[14] On the other hand, a 1°C. increase in temperature and a 10 percent decrease in rainfall might reduce the wheat crop by 20 percent in the U.S. and the Soviet Union.[15]

One of the most widely accepted weather indicators is sunspots. Every 22 years, in a so-called Hale cycle, they return to their magnetic starting point. And over the years, droughts have occurred in a similar pattern.[16] The value of this knowledge is limited, however, because droughts do not occur exactly on schedule, and they also occur at other times in the cycle.

But most weather experts are primarily concerned with man-induced changes, especially the increase in carbon dioxide in the atmosphere. At present, our atmosphere contains a relatively modest 335 parts per million (ppm) of CO_2. But due to increased burning of fossil fuels, that level is expected to almost double by 2050.[17] Since CO_2 does not absorb much of the short-wave radiation from the sun, but does absorb a considerable part of the heat radiation from the Earth, this increase in CO_2, through the so-called greenhouse effect, could raise the temperature on earth significantly.

A recent study by seven atmospheric scientists from the National Aeronautics and Space Administration (NASA) argues that there has been an overall warming trend in global weather extending back to 1880, and the study links this trend to CO_2 build-up in the atmosphere. The scientists predict a warming of "almost unprecedented magnitude" over the next century, which among other things would cause extensive disruption of agriculture.[18] These conclusions were supproted by a report that the summer Antarctic ice pack decreased by 2.5 million square kilometers between 1973 and 1980.[19] But the findings and projections of the NASA study are already the subject of considerable debate.

Some rather elaborate disaster scenarios have been constructed from this possibility. For example, if a CO_2 increase led to a 2°C. rise in Earth's temperature, the polar areas would likely experience even greater warming, while temperatures in the tropics would show little change. If the West Antarctic ice sheet—the most unstable portion of the world's ice mass—melted as a result of this heat wave, it would raise the world sea level 15 to 20 feet. This rise would inundate more than one-fourth of the states of Florida and Louisiana, and Boston, New York City, and Atlantic City would suffer similar fates. Parts of Texas, Virginia, Delaware and Washington, D.C. would be flooded. Billions of dollars worth of property would be destroyed, along with some important food-producing areas.[20]

But that's a big if. While CO_2 levels seem certain to rise, the resulting temperature may be offset by Earth's natural cooling cycle. Or changes in temperature could cause an increase in cloud cover, resulting in a lower surface temperature in another area.[21] So while most scientists suggest that some warming will result from the CO_2 increase, nobody knows how much or what impact this might have.

Another worry is the possible deterioration of the ozone layer around the earth, which protects us from damaging ultraviolet radiation. In the stratosphere, ozone is normally fairly stable. But when chlorofluoro-carbons (CFC's)—man-made chemicals that help refrigerators keep cool and propel aerosol sprays—reach the stratosphere, a complicated series of chemical reactions take place that converts some of the ozone to oxygen. Computer models suggest that the eventual ozone layer depletion may range from 5 to 28 percent.[22]

The increase in ultraviolet radiation reaching earth would not only increase incidences of skin cancer, it would lower yields from both farms and fisheries. Experiments show that some crops— including sugar beets, tomatoes and corn—might be "significantly affected" by a 16 percent ozone depletion.[23]

A weather-related problem that already affects food production is acid rain. This is caused by gaseous pollutants such as sulfur and nitrogen oxides, which combine with atmospheric oxygen to produce dehydrated sulfuric and nitric acid.[24] These pollutants are sometimes sent high into the air by tall smokestacks, and travel hundreds of miles before falling.

Acid rain has destroyed all the fish in more than 100 lakes in the Adirondack area alone.[25] Its effect on agriculture is somewhat unclear, but indications are that it can harm crops in two ways. First, it can damage the leaves of plants, affecting their photosynthesis. Second, it makes soil more acidic. While this can benefit some crops, such as tomatoes and strawberries, the overall effect is detrimental.[26]

Finally, there is the problem of desertification. Around the planet, man helps turn an area the size of Maine into desert every year.[27] Drought is a contributing factor, but the primary causes of desertification are expanding agriculture into areas that are not suitable for normal farming, ill-planned irrigation that causes soil salinity, overgrazing, and over-collection of wood. Because of these destructive habits, 19 percent of the land surface of the world is threatened by desertification. At present rates of degradation, we will lose one-third of the planet's arable land by the year 2000.[28]

The land area affected by desertification in North America is surprisingly large. Harold Dregne, head of the International Center for Arid and Semi-Arid Land Studies at Texas Tech University, calculated that 1.1 million square miles, or 36.8 percent of the continent's arid lands, have undergone "severe" desertification. Some 10,500 square miles of the continent have undergone "very severe" desertification, according to Dregne. By contrast, Africa's "severe" desertification totals 4 million square miles, but its "very severe" desertification is less than North America's—5500 square miles.[29]

This estimate suggests that approximately 10 percent of the U.S. land mass is in a state of severe or very severe desertification. The actual acres threatened by severe desertification, however, are almost twice that amount.

Despite our technology—and also because of it—climate-related problems will continue to occur. The potential for serious trouble is not small; drought alone could disrupt our entire food system. And it is certain that climate-related problems throughout the world will put considerable stress on our food supplies in the years ahead.

11
Nutrition/Health

The most important function of any food system is to provide adequate nutrition to the people it serves. The best measure of success is not yields per acre, or number of varieties of food available, but whether *all* the people are properly fed. From this perspective, the U.S. food system is seriously lacking.

Despite our food abundance, good nutrition is *not* available to all the people in the United States. There are two basic reasons: lack of money, and lack of education about food. Until recent years, our concern was under-nutrition. (Many Americans still suffer from hunger. See "Food Assistance.") Today, with 40 percent of American women and 32 percent of American men aged 40 to 49 technically classified as "obese," malnourishment can refer to overconsumption of food as well as to the consumption of dangerous food ingredients.[1]

In recent decades, our diet has changed dramatically. Since 1910, per capita consumption of fresh fruit has fallen 33 percent, while consumption of processed fruit has increased over 300 percent.[2] People now eat 74 percent fewer fresh potatoes than they did in 1910, but potato chip consumption rose 71 percent from 1959 to 1970.[3] During this same decade, milk consumption dropped 20 percent,[4] while consumption of soft drinks climbed 157 percent.[5] Americans now eat twice as much refined sugar (sucrose) as their great-grandparents did.[6]

There is growing evidence that directly connects our food habits with disease. Cardiovascular disease can be attributed partly to excess saturated fat and refined carbohydrates in the diet.[7] Tooth decay in children and young adults has likewise been linked to refined carbohydrates[8] and sugar consumption has been linked with obesity and diabetes.[9] High intake of salt may contribute to high blood pressure and its attendant ills—stroke, congestive heart failure and kidney disease.[10]

Epidemiologic and laboratory data suggest that diet is an important cancer-causing factor, and it is correlated to more than half of all cancers in women and at least one-third of all cancers in men.[11] Lack of cellulose and other fiber in the typical U.S. diet is suspected of increasing the frequency of diverticulitis and colonic cancer.[12] In addition, increased fat consumption is linked to a high level of colon and breast cancers.[13]

The human body is designed to run on unprocessed foods, and some of the ingredients in our present diet are alien to our system. As a result, it is reasonable to question the wisdom of eating a high percentage of refined foods. Of the eight leading causes of death (See chart 1) in the United States, four have a strong causal link to the typical diet of high-fat, overly-processed foods.[14] A fifth illness, cirrhosis of the liver, is directly connected to alcohol abuse and subsequent malnourishment.[15]

Increased mortality is not the only factor to consider. The medical bills caused by poor nutrition are enormous. In 1980, Americans spent over $500 million on antacid medications to assist their digestive systems.[16] Direct health care costs in the United States were about $192 billion in 1978, or $878 for each person. These direct costs include detection of disease, treatment, rehabilitation, research and training.[17]

Indirect costs, such as those due to losses from employment or homemaker services, are also substantial. Consider just the following: circulatory system diseases are estimated to cost $60.4 billion for direct costs, $44.3 billion for indirect costs; cancer is estimated to cost $22.3 billion—$5.3 billion for direct costs, $17 billion for indirect costs; alcohol abuse is estimated to cost $44.2 billion—$11.9 billion for direct costs, $32.3 billion for indirect costs.[18]

Even these dollar figures, huge as they are, miss the human dimension of the problem. Millions of men and women suffer needless discomfort and pain every day, and many die prematurely. It is a continuing scandal that in America, a land flowing with food, so many people are improperly nourished.

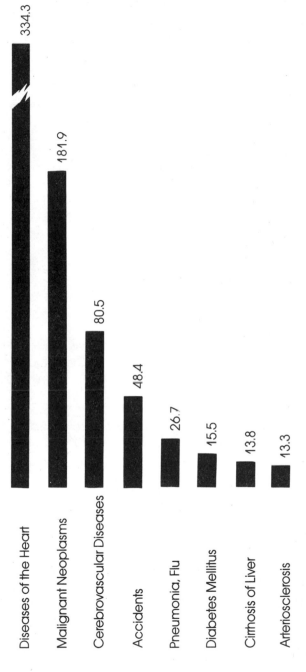

CHART #1
LEADING CAUSES OF DEATH IN THE UNITED STATES (1978)
(RATES PER 100,000)

Cause	Rate
Diseases of the Heart	334.3
Malignant Neoplasms	181.9
Cerebrovascular Diseases	80.5
Accidents	48.4
Pneumonia, Flu	26.7
Diabetes Mellitus	15.5
Cirrhosis of Liver	13.8
Arteriosclerosis	13.3

Source: U.S. Department of Commerce, Bureau of the Census *Statistical Abstract of the U.S., 1980*, p. 79, U.S. Government Printing Office, Washington, D.C.

12
Food Processing

In the beginning, food was processed primarily for preservation. Sometime after 4000 B.C., the Egyptians developed a fermented sourdough wheat bread which would keep for months without spoiling. Other natural preservation methods such as drying, salting, and smoking were known and practiced as early as 3000 B.C. The first commercial-scale processing began during the Roman Empire with the production of bread, wine, fruit preserves, cheese, bacon, and olive oil.[1]

Today, while processing for preservation is still important, many products are processed for convenience. Over 75 percent of the food Americans eat is processed in some way,[2] from waxed apples to frozen TV dinners. In the last 50 years, per capita consumption of processed fruits and vegetables has risen 300 percent while consumption of their fresh counterparts has decreased 33 percent.[3] During this same period, consumption of frozen potato products has increased 700 percent.[4]

There are several reasons for the popularity of processed, "convenience-type" foods. People want food which can be prepared quickly, with less time and effort than dishes created "from scratch." Greater affluence, decreasing household size, and the spread of microwave ovens have encouraged the use of convenience foods. In 1978, convenience foods accounted for one-third of consumer food expenditures.[5]

Processing extends the shelf life of many foods, increasing the time they are available to shoppers. It also destroys microorganisms which might otherwise be harmful to health. But food processing has taken its toll in tremendous expenditures of energy, loss of nutrients, higher retail prices, and possible health hazards.

74

Food processing takes almost one-third of the energy used in the U.S. food system, consuming 1.8 million barrels of oil equivalent per day.[6] About 1000 calories of energy are expended for each calorie of processed food we consume. This energy is used to wash, cut, steam, boil, freeze, dry, mill, refine, bake, can and package food. Beet sugar production is the most energy intensive processing operation, using about 8.5 percent of all food processing energy, while poultry and egg processing uses about 0.5 percent of the total. Frozen fruits and vegetables take about twice as much energy for processing as their canned counterparts.[7]

This energy consumption is passed on to the consumer in higher food prices. The more highly processed the food, the more it costs. Potatoes are a good example:

Fresh potatoes	$ .29/lb.
Canned potatoes	.33/lb.
Frozen potatoes	.70/lb.
Instant Mashed potatoes	1.39/lb.
Potato Buds	1.76/lb.
Lay's Potato Chips	2.44/lb.
Pringle's Potato Chips	2.58/lb.[8]

Manufacturers often promote their most highly processed products, since these return the greatest profits.

Another drawback is the nutrient losses that occur during processing. In the canning of green beans, for example, approximately 45 percent of the vitamin B-1 is lost; with tomatoes about 30 percent of the vitamin C is lost.[9] During the refining process, white flour is robbed of most of its vitamins, minerals, iron and fiber, and iron and B-vitamins must be replaced through enrichment. In the United States, enrichment of milled cereal products is mandated in 30 states.[10]

In recent years, it has become common practice to fortify processed foods with vitamins and minerals. Fortification does boost nutritional value, but it also increases cost, and many of these foods still lack fiber, and are high in fat, sugar, salt, or other additives. (See "Nutrition/Health.")

Indeed, the use of food additives has skyrocketed in recent years. About 2700 are now in use, a jump of 40 percent over 1970.[11] Shipments of additives were valued at $1.3 billion in 1978, and are estimated to reach $4.5 billion by 1990.[12] These additives are used to enhance flavor, improve texture and appearance, heighten color, retain or boost nutritional value, prevent spoilage, and sweeten artificially. The average American consumes his weight (about 139 pounds) in additives per year, primarily sugar, salt, and corn syrup.[13]

While most food additives are safe, some have negative health effects from long-term use at low exposure levels. A small number, including Violet Dye No. 1 and Red Dye No. 2, have been banned from use as suspected cancer-causing agents.[14] Most food labels now provide a complete listing of food additives, but it is difficult for consumers to know which of those compounds are harmless and which of them may be dangerous.

The final step in food processing is packaging. In 1980, Americans paid more than nine percent of their total food expenditures—some $34 billion—for packaging.[15] While packaging often provides necessary protection, and makes handling more convenient, many packages cost more than the foods they contain. Beer cans cost five times as much as the brew they hold, while soft drink cans, chewing gum wrappers and breakfast cereal boxes cost about twice as much as their contents. At the other end of the spectrum, butter, cheese and poultry packaging costs less than 10 percent of the food ingredients.[16]

Part of the high cost of some packaging reflects the energy needed to produce it. 1.3 percent of the nation's energy consumption is used for packaging.[17] It takes 1643 calories of energy, for example, to produce a 12-ounce aluminum pop-top soda can which contains a drink with 150 calories of food energy.[18]

Processing and packaging food keeps it safe from many old enemies, such as mold, decay, and dangerous microorganisms. But these activities burn vast amounts of energy, and they have created some new threats, such as harmful additives, decreased nutritional value, higher prices. Increasing reliance on heavily processed and packaged food can only lead to inflated food costs, excessive energy waste, and deteriorating health.

13
Fisheries

Fish provide 5.4 percent of the world's protein, more than the amount provided by beef, or pork, or eggs.[1] United States per capita use of fish and shellfish was 51 pounds in 1980, and about half of that amount was used as human food.[2] The demand for fish is increasing, but it is questionable whether even our present levels of production are sustainable.

The U.S. fishing industry employs some 277,000 people, and it contributed $7 billion to the GNP in 1980.[3] Since 1945, the U.S. fish catch has increased 41 percent. At the present time, 56 percent of the fish landed here are eaten by people; the rest are used for industrial purposes—generally as livestock, pet, or poultry feed.[4]

Despite controlling some of the world's richest fishing grounds, (almost one-fifth of the world's main fisheries resources are within 200 miles of the U.S. coasts), the United States imports almost 50 percent of its fish, and most of the imports are used for human food.[5] Competition for this supply is likely to intensify, since the United Nations predicts that world fish demand will increase 50 percent by the year 2000.[6] Significantly, about three-fourths of the increase in U.S. fish catch in the last three decades has been of lower-quality fish used for animal feed.[7]

The most serious problem confronting our fisheries is depletion of stocks. Despite the establishment of the 200-mile Fishery Conservation Zone, an area in which foreign fishing is restricted, U.S. fishermen are still concentrating their efforts on a few intensively-fished species. Just seven varieties of fish—menhaden, tuna, salmon, hakes, flounder, alewives and cod—account for 74 percent of the U.S. catch.[8] And while there is little potential to increase harvest of these species, there are a large number of species in the Fishery Conservation Zone which remain underutilized.

Intensive fishing of a small number of species not only depletes the stocks of these fish, it also drives up prices, and "wastes" the unconventional species which are used as food in other countries. Worldwide, 21 species of commercial grade fish have already been depleted by overfishing.[9] Meanwhile, in the United States, so-called "trash fish" make up a sizeable portion of all fish caught. East coast fishermen have reported that 30 percent of their catch is of undesirable or non-traditional species which are often discarded at sea and frequently killed in the process.[10]

Energy use presents another challenge. The U.S. fishing fleet uses 27 calories of fuel energy to harvest one calorie of fish protein.[11] Each year, over $400 million worth of fossil fuels are used to build and operate commercial fishing vessels.[12] A major factor in the increasing rate of fuel use is the increasing amount of time spent searching for fish. In 1980, 54 percent (by dollar value) of the U.S. catch was made more than three miles offshore.[13]

Another reason for increased energy use is the trend toward bigger boats. A large vessel uses considerably more fuel energy than a number of smaller vessels with an equivalent harvesting capacity. For example, 22 fifteen-ton boats have the same capacity as a single 333-ton boat, but the small boats are 44 percent more energy efficient in obtaining the same catch.[14] In addition, small vessels employ more people and are more adaptable than large vessels.

Specialization—fishing for one particular species—further decreases energy efficiency, since fishermen must fish longer to catch what they want. The more specialized the fisherman, the more energy is wasted. Lobster and shrimp fishermen, for example, use over 150 calories of fuel energy for each calorie of protein harvested. On the average, one-half gallon of diesel fuel is used to harvest a single one-pound lobster which will yield a quarter pound of lobster meat.[15]

Our fishing grounds are also damaged by water pollution. The Environmental Protection Agency received reports of 425 pollution-caused fish kills in U.S. waters between 1961 and 1975,[16] and these *reported* incidents are only a fraction of the total deaths. Sublethal concentrations of various pollutants can interfere with fish behavior and physiology, increase the incidence of disease, and change migration patterns.

Even though the world's oceans provide 98 percent of our fish, we use them as dumping grounds. Five million tons of petroleum hydrocarbons leak, spill or are dumped into the oceans each year,[17] an amount equivalent to 35 million barrels of oil. Seven million tons of litter are discarded annually into the oceans. Heavy metals such as mercury, copper, zinc, cadmium and lead are turning up in increasing amounts, and these minerals are highly toxic to fish and to the people who eat the fish.

The cost of this pollution is only now becoming apparent. Environmental changes on the Connecticut shoreline have resulted in losses of over $1 billion in shellfish revenues. In 1975 alone, U.S. fishermen lost over $37 million in potential income because of shellfish acreages that were closed by pollution.[18] But the most significant impact on fisheries is from chronic, low-level pollution sources which have a considerable lag time. The impact of pollutants entering our waters now will be most serious in coming years.[19]

Development is a growing threat to many coastal fishing areas. Tidal marshes, estuaries and other shore areas which are essential to our fisheries are also in demand for recreational and residential purposes. Some 60 to 80 percent of all commercial marine fish species are dependent on estuarine ecosystems during at least part of their lifetimes. At the same time, 60 percent of the U.S. population is concentrated in coastal counties.[20] When there is a conflict, development pressures usually win out over fishery interests.

Coastal development, water pollution and intensive fishing of a few species have put increasing pressure on our fish stocks. When these problems are coupled with rising fuel costs and decreasing energy efficiency, we can see clearly that our fishing industry is in serious trouble. If we do not make significant changes in the management and methods of fishing, we are likely to squander this crucial protein source.

14
Forest Resources

Trees are an important part of our food system. They are the source of fruits, nuts, legumes and roughage, and they provide packaging materials for food. Trees also produce wood for construction, energy and heating purposes.

Trees are often accused of taking up land that might otherwise be used for farming. But they play an important role in soil building, and improve local atmospheric conditions by lowering summer air temperatures, increasing humidity and rainfall, and decreasing wind velocities. They use land too hilly or rocky to farm. In short, forests are an essential part of our agriculture system.

At the present time the world's forests are being cut faster than they are growing. And although annual tree growth in the United States exceeds the annual harvest, this country is partly responsible for deforestation in other parts of the world.

About one-third of the United States is forestland and two-thirds of this amount is classified as commercial timberland—land capable of producing commercial crops of timber.[1] On a per-acre basis, the United States has the most productive forest in the world; it is second in terms of commercial forest volume and third in area of commercial farmland.[2] The harvest value of domestic timber is over $6 billion each year.[3]

Despite this wealth of forests, the United States has been a net importer of wood since 1950.[4] Imports have been rising steadily. In 1978, the United States imported 3.7 billion cubic feet of wood, a quarter of all the wood consumed that year.[5] Imports are expected to double by 1990.[6]

These imports contribute to deforestation in many countries. Not only does the United States use large amounts of foreign wood,

80

but we import 100,000 tons of beef from Central American countries each year—countries which are cutting down their forests at a frightening rate to open up grazing land for cattle production.[7]

This deforestation also has a negative effect on the Earth's atmosphere. Forests are like human lungs in reverse: they take in carbon dioxide and give off oxygen. Since forests store 90 percent of the total carbon in our global ecosystem, even small changes in the world forest cover have a significant effect on atmospheric carbon dioxide levels. (See "Climate.") In the tropics, land clearance is occurring so rapidly that it contributes more carbon dioxide to the atmosphere each year than the worldwide combustion of fossil fuels.[8]

While global demands for wood are increasing, our own forest reserves are shrinking, making the United States less able to meet even its present needs. U.S. forestlands are being converted to other uses at a rate of 1.5 million acres each year.[9] Globally, deforestation is occurring at a rate of 50 million acres yearly—an area the size of the state of Washington.[10]

Forest management is another problem. Under current management practices, commercial forestlands are producing less than half the net growth that could be attained in correctly stocked natural stands.[11] Farmland and miscellaneous private lands, which make up 60 percent of the commercial forestland in the United States, currently contribute only 50 percent of the nation's saw timber harvest.[12]

Much of the privately held forestland is divided into parcels which are considered too small to be profitably harvested. This judgment, however, is partly due to the lack of financial incentives for managing and selling timber. The Forest Service's policies for selling logging rights in National Forests help keep timber prices at low levels. In many cases, the Forest Service sells timber at prices below operating costs, since they sell according to calculated market value without making allowances for longterm management costs such as reforestation. This policy subsidizes the forest industry with taxpayer dollars, encourages timber cutting in the National Forests, and depresses timber prices, discouraging private landowners from making investments in timber management.

In most forestlands, pesticide and erosion problems have not been as severe as they are in croplands. Pesticide use in forests accounts for less than 5 percent of the nation's total consumption.[13] United States timber lands have an average soil loss of 1.2 tons per acre. But in six states—Arkansas, Georgia, Hawaii, Illinois, Ohio and

West Virginia—erosion rates on grazed forestlands are over 11 tons per acre.[14] And in many incidents, the spraying of pesticides, herbicides and defoliants has been destructive to wildlife and to human health.

If the United States demand for timber leads to increased domestic production, it is likely that this good record will be tarnished, however. Increasing reliance on artificial regeneration, row-planting of genetically similar species, clearcutting, dependence on pesticides, herbicides, and chemical fertilizers, and use of large machinery will intensify the problems of soil erosion and wildlife destruction.

As long as the United States is dependent on foreign timber, we cannot rightfully claim that a "conservation ethic" is preventing us from using our own forests more fully. Because of our high per capita use of timber, the preservation of our forests is now occurring at the expense of forests elsewhere. Trees are essential, not only for the food and wood they provide, but also for the oxygen they provide and the carbon dioxide they clean from the air. Slow destruction of the world's forests means slow destruction for our entire environment.

15
Urban Food Systems

About 74 percent of the U.S. population lives in metropolitan areas.[1] These built-up areas have not been designed to include a basic food resource for the community, and virtually all food must be imported from a considerable distance. In the past, our food system has been so successful in producing an abundant and dependable supply that city dwellers generally take food for granted and do not think about where it comes from or how it is produced.

Feeding a city is no easy task. Philadelphia, with a population of 1,755,000,[2] consumes 2.6 billion pounds of food each year, or over 7 million pounds every day.[3] Hauling this amount of food into the city requires more than 175 trucks each day.[4] Philadelphia residents spent nearly $1.8 billion for their food in 1980,[5] $95 million of which is for transportation.[6] More than 70 percent of the city's food comes from outside the state of Pennsylvania.[7]

Because cities are so food-dependent, announcing "food shortage" in a metropolitan area could lead to disaster. Stores would be emptied almost immediately and large segments of the populace would be left without food. But the design of our system has set the stage for this to happen.

This vulnerability is relatively new. Specialty crops—fruits, vegetables, nuts, mushrooms—have traditionally been produced near urban areas, making intensive use of land, and yielding higher economic returns per acre than most other types of agriculture. In 1978, 23 percent of all U.S. farms were located within Standard Metropolitan Statistical Areas.[8] At that time, these metropolitan agricultural areas produced 26 percent of the value of all commodities sold in the 48 contiguous states.[9]

Agricultural land near urban areas is rapidly disappearing,

83

however. During the years from 1967 to 1975, 16.6 million acres of farmland were converted to urban and built-up uses, and 6.7 million acres were permanently flooded. About 5.4 million acres had been cropland, and of this, 4.8 million acres were taken for cities, villages, industrial sites, railroad yards, cemeteries, airports, golf courses and other uses requiring more than 10 acres. And for every acre that is taken for urban uses, another acre is idled and isolated by noncontiguous development. On this basis, urbanization may have actually taken nearly 10 million acres out of cropland from 1967 to 1975.[10]

Suburban sprawl not only occupies land, it also increases taxes for the remaining farms. Land values soar and profitability decreases. Unstable conditions make farmers reluctant to make improvements and further investments. They have no incentives to practice conservation and improvement measures. This in turn makes the farm less attractive as a farm, and more inaccessible to those who want to enter farming.

New suburbanites sometimes object to many agricultural practices, and make it difficult for farmers to work. Such things as use of pesticides, fertilizers, and herbicides, livestock odors and wastes, noisy tractors and equipment, and escaped livestock are sources of contention. Farmers, on the other hand, must deal with air pollution and congestion caused by automobiles, theft, vandalism, and the disruption of family farm life and values. The easy solution is to sell and relocate away from population centers, or simply sell and take a regular job. So that is what often happens.

But every time a farm near a metropolitan area is lost, the situation worsens. People must have food, and the long-distance system that supplies our urban areas is seriously deficient. Without more local food sources, any supply breakdown will mean hunger in our cities.

16
Food Assistance

Today one in every eight Americans is poor. According to the Census Bureau, the number of poor people in America now stands at more than 29 million, a jump of 3.2 million between 1979 and 1980.[1] Access to food is one of their most serious problems. While it is true that the average person in the U.S. spends less than 15 percent of their disposable income on food, the poor spend close to 40 percent.[1a]

It seems inconceivable that in a country with such a sophisticated and elaborate food production and distribution system, hunger and malnutrition still exist. But a recent National Food Consumption Survey showed that fewer than 10 percent of poor families received all their Recommended Daily Allowances (RDA's) of essential nutrients. Less than 50 percent received even two-thirds of their daily requirements.[2]

The barriers which deny poor people a nutritious, affordable diet fall into three categories: 1) lack of means; 2) lack of access to competitively priced foods; and 3) lack of nutrition education. All of these problems are being addressed to some degree, but the success of government's efforts to end hunger has been rather mixed.

Federal food assistance had its beginning in the food distribution program, established in 1935 to aid farmers who could not find markets for excess products. The government bought the food and gave it to poor families.[3]

Things have come a long way since then. Today the U.S. Government sponsors 13 major programs which provide food or food assistance. Among these programs are Food Stamps, School Lunch and Breakfast, Special Milk, Child Care Food, Summer Food,

Women, Infants and Children (W.I.C.), Elderly Feeding and Food Distribution. In 1976, federal expenditures for all food programs were over $8 billion, a seven fold increase from 1967.[4] In fiscal 1981, the U.S.D.A., which administers most of these programs, spent $16.6 billion—more than 60 percent of its budget[5]—on food assistance, more than $75.00 for every person in the United States.

While government food programs have helped reduce hunger and malnutrition in the United States, they face considerable problems. Many needy, eligible people don't participate in the programs because they don't know about them, or for varied reasons they choose not to join. Those who do participate often receive benefits below the subsistence level. The effectiveness of food assistance programs, especially Food Stamps, has been reduced by the mass exodus of supermarkets from inner cities and the lack of supermarkets in rural areas. As a result, poor people in these places must purchase higher-priced and lower quality food from smaller, local grocers. Lack of adequate nutrition education puts the poor at greater nutritional risk since they often are unaware of relationships between diet and health. And the effect of these difficulties—lack of resources, markets and information—is to perpetuate hunger and malnutrition among America's poor.

A closer look at some specific programs brings these problems into sharper focus.

The Food Stamp Program (FSP) is the primary federal effort to help low-income households afford adequate diets. It does this by increasing income, in the form of stamps that can be used only for food purchases. The program was mandated by the Food Stamp Act of 1964, and is administered by the USDA. Last year the FSP served almost 23 million people, and the 1981 budget is nearly $11.5 billion.[6]

With so many people now receiving food stamps, the economic repercussions of the program are extensive. For every $1.00 in food stamp benefits spent, there is an additional $3.64 worth of economic activity, 35 cents worth of economic retail sales and 42 cents worth of farm sector revenues.[7] Overall, food stamp spending generates an additional $4.2 billion annually in retail food sales, above what would have been spent by poor people without food stamps. Food stamp spending also generates an additional $1.7 billion in farm income.[8]

Since its founding, the FSP has undergone major modifications in its policy, eligibility requirements, and administration. Until the late 1970's, participants in the program were required to purchase food stamps. (For example, $25 had to be spent to obtain $50 worth of stamps.) Now, however, stamps may be obtained free. That change brought in 3 million new participants in 1978 alone, including many elderly and rural residents, and people so poor they did not have the cash to purchase coupons under the old system.[9] The food stamp budget rose accordingly, with 1981 expenditures more than double the 1976 level.

Despite this growth, however, estimates are that the FSP reaches only 60 percent of those eligible.[10] And for those who do receive the stamps, the funding level is far from adequate.

The average American family of four spends about $400 per month for food at home. Yet the average food stamp family of four, with a monthly income of $320, gets only $158 worth of food stamps per month.[11] With no income whatsoever, a four-person household could receive a maximum of $233 worth of food stamps each month.[12] Yet the absolute lowest food budget required to purchase a healthful diet for a family of four (includes children, aged 6-8 and 9-11), according to July, 1981, USDA figures, is $246.50.[13]

Consequently, the average food stamp family receiving $158 worth of stamps can only obtain about two-thirds of its daily nutritional requirements. The USDA acknowledges that only about 16 percent of those spending at this level will obtain adequate diets.[14]

As costs rise, the plight of food stamp families worsens. From September, 1976, to November, 1979, the average gross income of food stamp households rose 17 percent, but the cost of living went up 32 percent. Meanwhile, the average per capita income of the U.S. population rose about 40 percent.[15] Despite these inadequacies, federal cutbacks in the food stamp budget have begun, and these will exacerbate existing problems, and affect retailers and farmers as well as recipients. Cutbacks may have serious consequences for supermarkets, especially those which obtain 5 percent or more of their total sales from food stamps. Food stamps now account for an average of 3 percent of total sales for both chain stores and independent retail stores, equivalent to about $3 billion in revenue for each type of store for 1980.[16] Farmers stand to lose over $650 million in revenue.[17]

But the biggest losers will be the recipients themselves. Under the Reagan Administration's plan, eligibility will be based on gross income rather than net income, and about 1 million people will lose food stamps completely. The remaining 21.6 million recipients will have their benefits reduced.[18] Despite these cuts, the food stamp program will increase $500 million in fiscal 1982, as cuts in other federal programs for the poor push more people onto food stamps or make them eligible for higher benefits.[19]

In addition to budgetary and administration complexities in food assistance programs, fraud and mismanagement, especially in the FSP, account for the loss of $1.6 billion.[19] If this massive fraud could be stopped, cutbacks would be unnecessary. Studies have shown that about 10 percent of all stamps are obtained illegally, primarily through thefts of authorizations to purchase (ATP) food stamps.[20] A special Washington-based unit, composed of officials from the Justice Department, USDA and the U.S. Postal Service, has recently been established to coordinate investigations of large-scale fraud in the FSP around the country.

The National School Lunch Program, which provides free or reduced cost meals to 26.7 million children every school day, will also be scaled down. Since eligibility for free meals is tied to food stamp eligibility, those children whose families are eliminated from the FSP will no longer be entitled to free school lunches. Depending on family income, they may be eligible for reduced-priced meals, the cost of which will probably rise from 20 cents to 40 cents.[21]

Finally, there is the question of whether these cutbacks in food assistance will actually save money. A case in point is the W.I.C. program, which provides specified food supplements to pregnant women, mothers, infants and children. At present, it reaches only 1.4 million of the more than 11 million persons eligible, and one-third of all counties in the nation still have no W.I.C. program.[22] Yet a study by the Harvard School of Public Health found that the United States saves $3.00 in avoiding hospital costs for newborn infants for every $1 spent on the W.I.C. program.[23]

Despite good intentions, the U.S. food assistance programs are not really working. More and more people are becoming eligible for help, the cost of food is increasing, and hunger and malnutrition persist. The problems of the poor—lack of food, bad housing, inadequate education, and unemployment—are mutually rein-forcing. Each one percent increase in unemployment, for example, adds from 1 to 1.3 million persons to the Food Stamp Program and costs the government $580 million in benefits.[24] Until we can break the cycle of hopelessness caused by the inequitable distribution of income in this country, the need for food assistance will continue.

17
International Dimensions

Without U.S. food exports, the problem of hunger and malnutrition around the world would be far worse. Many countries would need to alter their diet completely. Meat consumption in Japan, Europe, and the Soviet Union would plummet, since American grain would no longer be available to feed livestock in these places.

At the same time, without foreign markets the U.S. food system would suffer considerably. Two out of every five cultivated acres in the U.S. is now planted in food for export. If these markets were not available, many farmers would be out of business, as huge surpluses drove prices below profitable levels. Extensive imports allow us to enjoy food that might otherwise be unavailable, and provide important income to the producing countries.

But these mutual benefits do not tell the whole story. Our food imports and exports have a number of negative side effects, both for the U.S. and its trading partners, especially those nations that are under-developed.

Food Imports

Although the United States is called the world's breadbasket, it is also a major importer of food. About 10 percent of our $300 billion 1980 food bill[1] paid for food grown outside this country.[2]

Some of that food—termed complementary imports—could not be grown easily here. These imports, primarily coffee, cocoa, and tropical fruits, accounted for less than half the total. A majority of our imports were supplementary—products such as meat, sugar, dairy products and grains, which could be produced here. Since 1975, our depedence on imports has grown 70 percent, with most of this increase coming in complementary foods.[3]

89

Transporting imported food to this country uses huge amounts of fuel. Long supply lines make these food sources especially vulnerable, either to shipping disruptions or local problems, such as political unrest or drought. And purchasing food overseas means the money does not go into the pocketbooks of America's farmers.

Imported food may also contain a hidden health threat. Pesticides that are restricted or banned in this country—including DDT, aldrin, and dieldrin—are often sold abroad legally, and may return on the coffee, bananas, and other food imports we buy. Occasional border checks show that at least 10 percent of all imported food is contaminated with illegal levels of pesticides.[4]

Further, the income from imported food may not benefit poorer countries as much as is often claimed. About 40 percent of our supplementary food imports come from developing countries—places that often have problems of hunger and malnutrition.[5] In many of these nations, the best land no longer grows food for local consumption, but export crops such as coffee, cocoa, rubber, and meat. During the 15 years from 1952 to 1967, for example, cotton acreage in Nicaragua quadrupled, while the cropland in basic grains was cut in half.[6] These changes may increase foreign exchange, but they have made many Third-World countries less able to feed themselves, and hence more dependent than ever on outside food.

Most of the agricultural exports from developing countries are shipped as raw materials. This practice means a low return to the farmer and little stimulation for local economic development. In contrast to manufactured goods, the prices paid on world markets for many raw products have declined in recent years. The price of bananas has fallen 30 percent in the last 20 years, while the price for cocoa has fluctuated widely, and had an overall decline of 80 percent since the 1950's.[7] When cash crops are produced for export, American farm technology is seldom far behind, despite the fact that it may not be appropriate for other countries. While highly productive, our food system is an intensive energy consumer. If all the world was fed on a U.S. diet produced with our current agricultural technology, food production alone would use up all the world's known petroleum reserves in just 11 years.[8]

Finally, the growing of cash crops for export has brought a range of local problems, including pesticide poisoning and environmental destruction. The World Health Organization estimates that half a million people are poisoned by pesticides each year.[9] In Costa Rica, which has tripled its beef production over the last 20 years to increase exports, about one-third of the forest and woodlands have been destroyed to provide for more pastureland. During this time, local per capita meat consumption has declined.[10]

Food Exports

The United States is the world's leading food exporter. Roughly half the agricultural products on the world market come from America, and this figure may rise to 60 percent over the next decade.[11] Total food exports are expected to reach $48 billion in 1981, up from $40.5 billion in 1980.[12]

This food plays an important role in improving our balance of payments, and may provide a $27 billion trade surplus in 1981.[13] Farm sales overseas account for 20 percent of farm income, and create nonfarm jobs for 630,000 workers. Forty percent of all the acres harvested in the United States produce food for export.[14]

These export sales are often heralded as an unadulterated good, providing numerous benefits to farmers and to the country. The current administration, in President Reagan's words, is "committed to the aggressive expansion of agricultural exports."[15]

Exports of grain and soybeans have grown very rapidly in the last 30 years. In 1950, we exported 15 million tons of grain; last year the total was 119 million tons.[16] In 1979, the United States exported 62 percent of its wheat production, 31 percent of its corn, 36 percent of its soybeans, 63 percent of its cotton, and 45 percent of its fats and oils.[17] Since 1970, U.S. exports of food grains have increased 350 percent.[18]

The majority of our exports—about two-thirds—go to industrial nations.[19] In recent years, while exports were skyrocketing, the amount of food aid has been declining. Only about 15 percent of U.S. food exports in developing countries are in the form of aid, compared to more than 50 percent 10 years ago.[20] The lion's share of our exports is in the form of feed grains, which go to developed countries to satisfy their craving for more meat.

While U.S. food aid is usually thought of in a humanitarian light, that is somewhat misleading. The original intent of Public Law 480, which created the Food for Peace Program, was to create and expand commercial markets for U.S. food in other countries.[21] Subsidized wheat exports under this program averaged 12 million tons a year during the early 1960s, when we had an extensive grain surplus. But as the world demand for grain increased, wheat aid fell to about five million tons annually by 1970.[22] At the present time, fully 85 percent of America's food exports to developing countries are on commercial terms.[23]

There is no doubt that U.S. food aid has helped feed millions of hungry people. But our export policy has also meant that many countries are now more dependent on our help than ever before. And with the world population increasing at about 70 million per year, the burden of trying to feed these people has proven to be a difficult one. In 1980, for the second year in a row, more grain was consumed worldwide than was produced,[24] but good harvests in 1981 may leave us with a surplus.

When a developing country increases its dependence on imported food, several things tend to happen. Traditional, subsistence agriculture is abandoned, and jobs in rural areas are lost. More people move into the cities, which are often overcrowded already. The temptation grows to neglect rural development and agriculture programs, and concentrate on other expenditures, such as military equipment. Monopolistic patterns of land ownership are reinforced, thereby widening the gap between rich and poor people.[25]

After a careful study of the situation, the Presidential Commission on World Hunger concluded:

> Self-reliance in the developing countries will never be achieved as long as U.S. agricultural policies continue to work against it. Only when the U.S. agricultural system is itself more self-reliant will the contradiction between U.S. domestic and international policies be reconciled. Far-reaching changes in current policies will be required if U.S. agriculture is to be restructured on a more self-reliant basis.[26]

Heavy farm exports are not an unmixed blessing to the United States, either. Because the world demand for surplus grain fluctuates considerably, exports have a major impact on domestic prices. During the years from 1972 to 1978, for example, when food exports increased dramatically, the prices farmers received for all crops varied five times as much as during the 1964 to 1971 period.[27]

When demand for grain is high, it pushes the price up, and two things happen. The price of grain in the United States increases, and poorer countries who desperately need food are sometimes priced out of the market. If current rates of exports continue until 1990, USDA economists predict it will result in an 85 percent increase in the price of wheat, corn, and soybeans.[28] And two economists at Columbia University recently concluded that the large grain sale to the Soviet Union in 1972 "cost American consumers a reduction of meat consumption valued at $3.3 billion by 1975."[29]

Along with our food exports, we are, in essence, exporting our topsoil. Most export crops are row crops, which are particularly susceptible to erosion. Already, national erosion rates for soybeans, corn, and wheat exceed the maximum tolerable rate, the level at which the soil's fertility can be maintained.[30] In 1980, about 2 billion tons of topsoil was eroded from U.S. farmland growing export crops.

By the turn of the century, exports alone may require an additional 110 million acres of cropland.[31] This will mean that more marginal land will be brought into production, and the erosion problem will worsen. In addition, this demand will contribute significantly to the land squeeze in this country, and all available land may be in production by the turn of the century.[32]

Finally, while American food exports make a positive contribution to our balance of payments, there is a problem here as well. For every dollar's worth of agricultural exports shipped abroad, we used about 25 cents' worth of imported oil to produce the food. In the near future the cost may rise to 40 cents.[33] So increased food production for export makes us more dependent on foreign oil.

U.S. food trade provides some important benefits to both American farmers and foreign consumers. But our current policies with imports and exports cause serious problems—higher world food prices, decreased self-reliance for other nations, and serious soil erosion in the U.S. While the world grows more dependent on our food, we are destroying the productive base that might supply this food.

What We Can Do About It

1
Goals for the U.S. Food System

The previous pages document the debilitating trends that are threatening the U.S. food system. They outline the full dimensions of our food system problems and, in total, make the alarming points that: 1) The situation is much more dangerous and immediate than most people realize; and 2) The combined effect of all these problems could collapse the system before any one of them becomes critical. Stated another way, all the parts of the food system may seem to be behaving rationally, but the whole system is irrational and non-sustainable.

As the title of our project and as this section make clear, there is an optimistic dimension to our point of view. Our food system faces serious challenges, but there are a host of responses that could transform it into a sustainable, efficient and economical organism which would create enormous benefits for American farmers, consumers, and businesses.

In order to judge which responses to our food system challenges we wish to implement, we need to know where we are going and, more importantly, where we *want* to be going.

In navigation, knowing where you want to go is at least as important as knowing where you are and how you will travel. Without a destination, navigation becomes meaningless. Without goals, the path becomes impossible to chart and progress cannot be measured because there are no benchmarks of present position or future goals. One of the reasons for the numerous problems of the U.S. food system is a lack of clear-cut, long and medium-range goals, a fact which makes navigation extremely difficult.

The Cornucopia Project's goals for the U.S. food system are presented as a tool for judging progress, and for helping decision-makers determine if the myriad individual decisions that need to be made in the course of normal food system activity are in the "right," or explicitly chosen, direction. Because some of the goals may be new to agriculture and the U.S. food system, or because they deal with larger systems and issues than the food system decision-maker is used to, they may strike some as an utopian vision. They are not utopian, in the depreciatory "pie-in-the-sky" use of the word. They are merely a longer-range and more holistic view of the functions of the U.S. food system. "Utopian" or "unrealistic" are names myopia-afflicted specialists apply to anything beyond the four feet in front of them or next quarter's profit margin. To avoid the pitfalls of resource depletion, environmental degradation, economic collapse, and eventual hunger, we need to do better than we have been doing. In today's world, there is nothing more unrealistic or romantic than the belief that all will be well if we look only at the short range.

The following goals are all inter-related and partially over-lapping. In total, they describe the food system behavior that The Cornucopia Project sees as most beneficial to the sustained vigor of the United States and its people—as well as those who depend on American food.

The Goals of the U.S. Food System Should Be:

1. **ABUNDANCE:** The food system should give every person access to adequate food—in quantity, quality and degree of choice.
2. **DEPENDABILITY:** The food system should provide every person with a reliable food supply—free from social, political, economic, or environmental disruption.
3. **SUSTAINABILITY:** The food system should be culturally, environ-mentally, economically, and technologically sustainable in respect to production and all other aspects of the food system—including resource inputs, cultivation techniques, processing and distribution.
4. **SAFETY:** The food system should not endanger workers, consumers or the environment.
5. **EFFICIENCY:** The food system should incur minimal energy or other resource costs.
6. **APPROPRIATENESS:** The food system should be matched to both the limits and needs of its region and locality.
7. **EQUITABILITY:** The food system's benefits should be available for use by all in a fair manner.
8. **WEALTH:** The food system should generate sufficient income

to rural people to provide a standard of living equivalent to that of other sectors of the economy to maintain vigorous rural communities and to enable farmers to fulfill their land stewardship responsibilities.

9. **FLEXIBILITY:** The food system should be open to change, growth, evolution, creativity and experimentation.

10. **OPENNESS:** The food system's organization, patterns of control and course towards the future should be within public view.

The current food system in the U.S. is not near those goals, and for the most part, not even heading in these directions. We need to re-think and re-establish what it is we want from our food system, and then proceed down the path that will take us toward our explicitly stated goals. Our goals are offered in the hope of opening and furthering a dialogue on where the U.S. food system *should* be heading.

How do we get from where we are to where we want to be? What paths exist for us to travel on? What new options could be and should be developed? What can we do in order to bring about a transition to a more sustainable, self-reliant food system with its accompanying economic and nutritional benefits? The next section seeks to answer these questions.

2
The Cornucopia Agenda: Finding the Path to Food Security

Developing a secure, affordable, and ecologically sustainable food supply will not be easy or simple. The U.S. food system is touched by so many factors: everything from the California food producer, fast-food restaurant, grocery store, food broker and warehouser to the backyard garden and family dinner table. It is affected by everything from federal, state and city government policies to business decisions to neighborhood and consumer organizations to individual actions.

Any thoughtful response to food system problems has to be on a variety of different levels. There are responses needed from agri-industry, from farmers, from the community, and from individuals. In addition, there are things we need to do immediately, and longer-range actions and emergency preparedness plans that must be developed. Nevertheless, The Cornucopia Project's research points out some relatively clear-cut paths that will lead us in the direction of our goals.

We have organized these paths or recommendations around the participants who need to carry them out: farmers, who produce our food; consumers, who are the foundation of the entire food system and who have the most power to change it; the food industry, which processes and distributes our food, and which has enormous powers for improving our food system in realtively short order; the cities, who would be hit hardest by any food crisis; the states, who have the power to do many of the things necessary for a secure food supply; and the nation, which has the overall power to coordinate the national dimensions of the food system, to enact the policies needed by the entire country, and to formulate sustainable relationships with the rest of the world.

100

The path The Cornucopia Project sees as leading the U.S. farmer to increasing economic success and strengthening the entire food system, has the following dimensions:

Recommendations — Farmers

1. REDUCE DEBT

Farmers can begin to gain liquidity in their business by reducing debt to manageable levels. Indebtedness is a cause of the vulnerability in today's farm operations. Many farmers are over a million dollars in debt; a 500 acre farm easily costs that much in today's inflated economy. A million dollars at 13 percent interest (if a farmer's lucky to get that low rate) is $130,000 annual interest, or about $356 a day. Such a farm is under a heavier cash flow burden than a 200 acre farm that's paid for.

Heavily indebted farmers are trapped into a spiraling complex of paying high interest costs, needing more acreage to increase cash flow, and relying on a heavy depreciation schedule to offset taxes on the large volume of production. They need to milk every possible cent from the land today with little thought for tomorrow. High depreciation, rather than frugal protection of assets, becomes the goal. Farmer indebtedness is a two-edged sword: if land prices fall precipitously—and remember there is no such thing in history as permanent inflation—such farmers will be financially wiped out.

2. DIVERSIFY PRODUCTION

Farmers can work toward selected combinations or rotations of crops, thus reducing fertilizer and weed control costs while giving the farm greater market stability. Single cash crop farmers (corn, wheat, hogs) are totally at the mercy of wild economic swings. With a mixture of crops, or even better, a mixture of crops and livestock, farmers would be in a better position to roll with the punches. they might lose money on one or two enterprises, but they will be able to make up for these losses with other crops. This will make them less vulnerable to variations in weather, pests and disease.

Tractor size can be reduced by spreading power requirements over a longer time period. With capital and production input costs increasing far more rapidly than the market value of the produce, diversification to increase the efficiency of those expensive resources is essential.

3. STOP SOIL EROSION

Farmers can become serious about stopping soil erosion.

Applying to the local soil conservation district for help in developing or updating a soil and water conservation management program would be a good start. Right now there is more money to be made by mining the soil than by saving it. Out from under the burden of 13 percent interest, and with public policy support for conservation, the farmer could take a slight short term "loss" for a big long term gain. Terraces, shelterbelts, grasslands, farming systems that build soil, and other soil saving stratagems, can become part of the farm plan again, reducing the need for increasingly costly fertilizer inputs.

4. CUT INPUTS

Farmers can use better management practices, such as cropping systems that reduce the need for chemical fertilizers and pesticides. They can minimize or eliminate the use of many expensive inputs and lower operating costs without significantly affecting yields. Through spending less money, they can make more.

5. CHANGE GRADING AND MARKETING STANDARDS

Farmers can begin to work for a change in those grading and marketing standards that are now outmoded. Many states do not yet allow the sale of certified raw milk, a more nutritious and as clean a product as pasteurized milk. The entire meat grading system, which gives incentives to corn-fed meat, needs overhauling. Excellent meat can be raised with a much higher percentage of pasture or roughage in the diet. But right now, this meat won't grade choice. Consequently, it brings a much lower price and provides, in effect, a subsidy for corn-fed meat production.

6. EXPLORE DIRECT MARKETING CHANNELS

Some farmers can sell food directly to the public. That way, they receive a higher price for what they sell, while consumers are often able to buy fresher food at lower cost.

7. DEVELOP ON-FARM ALTERNATIVE ENERGY SOURCES

Farmers can continue to investigate possibilities for using alternative energy sources. Raising oil crops to substitute for diesel fuel may already make economic sense. So might a team of horses in some operations. Some vegetables produced in solar greenhouses now seem economically competitive with vegetables brought in from long distances.

8. DEVELOP ON-FARM FERTILIZER SOURCES

Farmers can start growing much of their own fertilizer again in the form of nitrogen-fixing legumes and green manure crops. They can use crop rotations that reduce the amount of herbicides needed, and biological controls to replace or reduce pesticide use.

9. SELL TO FOOD SERVICE OUTLETS

A large percentage of food is consumed outside the home, at restaurants, schools, and other institutions. Many of these organizations buy food in large quantities, and could become good customers for marketing co-ops formed and operated by farmers. The trend toward salads and other fresh foods will enlarge opportunities for aggressive farmers to produce specifically for food service markets.

The path The Cornucopia Project sees as being the most economical, sustainable and safe for the U.S. food consumer, and which will benefit the whole food system most, has the following aspects:

Recommendations — Consumers

1. INCREASE AWARENESS OF FOOD SYSTEM OPERATION

Consumers can become more aware of where their food originates and what is done to it. Much of our food is transported a great distance; for every two dollars spent on energy to grow food, another dollar is spent on energy to move it around. By reading food labels and talking to grocery store personnel, consumers can learn much about their food.

2. CONSUME MORE FRESH, LOCALLY-GROWN FRUITS AND VEGETABLES

Consumers can purchase fresh, locally-grown fruits and vegetables when these foods are in season, and enjoy foods at the peak of their nutritional value during the time they are least expensive. By buying these foods in bulk and processing them for cold weather months consumers can eliminate the commercial processing and packaging costs that push up food prices.

3. SUPPORT LOCAL FARMERS

Consumers can help to create a more viable local agriculture by buying food directly from growers. By patronizing roadside stands, "pick your own" farms and orchards, and farmers' markets that sell locally-grown food, consumers can assure themselves of tasty, nutrition-packed foods at reasonable prices, while at the same time providing needed financial support to local farmers.

Consumers who live in cities can take advantage of the "support your neighborhood farmer concept" by joining a food co-op or buying club that contracts with farmers in the region. In addition, by buying in large quantities, food costs per unit will be lower, with the savings passed on to the consumer.

4. DEVELOP A PRUDENT DIET

Consumers can begin to gradually modify their diets to include less fat, salt, sugar, and cholesterol, and include more fiber and vegetable protein. According to the U.S. Dietary Goals, fat should be reduced from 40 to 30 percent of caloric intake, with saturated fat accounting for no more than 10 percent. Sugar should be reduced to 15 percent of calorie intake, salt use should be reduced to 3 grams per day, and cholesterol intake to 300 mg. per day. Carbohydrate consumption should be increased to 55 to 60 percent of caloric intake.[1]

5. GROW MORE FOOD

Consumers can grow their own fruits and vegetables. Already, 34 million American home gardeners produce some of their food.[2] Intensive gardening techniques could greatly expand the contribution from home gardens. When planning a garden, one possible strategy is to join with neighbors and plant some unusual fruits and vegetables. Then, by sharing this harvest, all will have a greater selection of food. In addition, this cooperation lays the groundwork for other activities, such as neighborhood canning and food storage.

6. PROCESS AND PRESERVE MORE FOOD

Consumers can process and preserve some of their—or the local farmer's—summer bounty by canning, freezing or drying their produce. By putting up their own food, consumers can control cooking and processing times, and the type and amounts of additives (if any) being used. Such foods will be of higher nutritional value than those bought in the supermarket, and they will also be cheaper.

7. EXTEND THE GROWING SEASON

Consumers can build solar grow frames or small greenhouses to extend their growing season. Grow frames are inexpensive, small structures that use the sun's heat and light so cool weather vegetables and salad greens can thrive even in mid-winter. During the coldest months, it is possible for a family to have a daily salad of fresh greens harvested from a grow frame. A greenhouse needs more space and is more costly to build, but it offers the consumer a wider selection of crops and a larger harvest.

8. PRODUCE MEAT OR FISH

Consumers can try raising backyard animals like rabbits, chickens, or fish. Chickens and rabbits take-up little space, are efficient converters of feed into meat, and their manures can be used as garden fertilizer. Fish gardening in a backyard or basement pool can provide a family with up to 100 pounds of fish a single growing season. Fish are excellent converters of food into protein, and these quiet, odorless creatures are a good choice for growing in suburban areas.

The path The Cornucopia Project sees as leading the U.S. food industry to increased economic viability, and strengthening the entire food system, has the following dimensions:

Recommendations — Food Industry

1. ENCOURAGE SUSTAINABLE FARMING METHODS

The food industry—companies that process, distribute, and market food—can encourage the use of more sustainable farming methods. Food companies can influence what farmers grow and how they grow it, as well as what is available in food stores and how much that food costs.

Processors could urge growers to use fewer chemicals, to minimize soil destruction, and even to grow more diversified crops. Food companies could give preferential treatment to farmers who follow such practices. Food waste could be cut considerably if the industry would de-emphasize the cosmetic aspects of produce, and focus on freshness and taste rather than uniform size and shape. Companies that can adapt to the changing realities affecting our system will increase their own chances for future success.

2. MINIMIZE ENERGY AND MATERIAL USE

The food industry can conserve energy and materials in several ways. Processing and packaging food, for example, use as much energy as all the farms that grow our food. Processing food less, and using simpler packaging, could cut energy and material use substantially. Additional savings could be made if distributors reversed the current trend toward truck transport, and made more use of railroads and piggyback transport, which are at least three times as energy efficient per ton/mile.

Incentives for the nation's railroads will also be needed so that their interstate capabilities can rise to meet increased demand. The results would not only be a saving of energy and money, but also the creation of a food system less vulnerable to disruption from an energy crisis.

3. REGIONALIZE FOOD PURCHASING, PROCESSING AND DISTRIBUTION

The food industry can work to regionalize operations. Many large companies process food in a few, very large plants, which increases the distance that food must be moved—both to and from the factory. By building new, more energy-efficient, smaller plants in farming areas or close to metropolitan areas where much of the food will be consumed, the food industry will save energy and money as well as help the local economy, farmer and consumer. And by decentralizing the purchasing of raw materials as much as possible, long distance shipping will be reduced and costs lowered.

4. PROMOTE CONSUMPTION OF FRESH, LOCALLY-PRODUCED FOOD

The food industry can de-emphasize advertising which features highly processed food with limited nutritional value, and promote locally-produced, fresh food in season. By encouraging consumption of this food, stores can not only enhance consumer nutrition, but the local economy as well.

5. WORK COOPERATIVELY WITH CONSUMERS

The food industry can stop seeing consumers as enemies. At present, consumers often feel food companies are solely concerned with selling products and making huge profits at their expense, while industry leaders tend to fear "radical consumer activists." Instead, the two groups should recognize their mutual dependence and work together. Consumers must recognize that food companies need to make a profit to exist, while the industry should realize that the goal of consumers is not to harass food companies, but to insure that they can buy good food at reasonable prices.

6. PROVIDE ADDITIONAL FOOD-RELATED SERVICES

The food industry can increase efforts to provide information to consumers, rather than merely trying to sell products. Stores that offer services beyond well-stocked shelves, such as nutrition education, hints for food preparation, and instructions for preserving fruits and vegetables, will stand out from their competition.

7. DEVELOP NEEDED NEW PRODUCTS

The food industry can develop new products that are in tune with a sustainable system, and that anticipate consumer needs and preferences in years to come. Products should fill an actual need, with emphasis on minimal packaging, less processing, and good nutritional value.

8. SEE FOOD IN A BROADER CONTEXT

The food industry cannot be just another business. Food does more than fuel people. Food nourishes life. People are recognizing more and more that what they eat affects their health and happiness. A growing number of people see diet as an essential component of a healthy life, and as a way to both treat and prevent illness. Over the past few years, consumers have substantially altered their diet for health reasons, and that trend is likely to continue. Companies that see food in a holistic way are likely to prosper.

The path The Cornucopia Project sees as leading urban areas to a secure, economical and sustainable food supply, and as strengthening the entire U.S. food system, has the following dimensions:

Recommendations — Cities

1. ESTABLISH A DEPARTMENT OF FOOD

Cities can establish, as part of their government, a "Department of Food" that is responsible for aiding and encouraging local food production and distribution. This department would:

   a. Regulate land use;

b. Encourage urban and rural food production;
c. Develop urban markets for local produce;
d. Coordinate waste recovery efforts;
e. Initiate educational programs; and
f. Develop plans for meeting local needs—both normal and emergency—through local production and storage.

Such departments would make urban food supplies more secure, and increase local food availability.

2. PRESERVE LAND

Cities can preserve the remaining farmland in their vicinity by:

a. Establishing land-use management committees to make policy recommendations dealing with urban growth while preserving farmland (or encouraging their zoning committees to do likewise).
b. Facilitating the establishment of urban block farms that include housing units with areas set aside for farming, greenhouses, food storage, food preservation, recycling, etc.
c. Creating "Agricultural Open Space Preserves" within their boundaries that preserve remaining prime farmland for agricultural use.

The more farmland that is preserved, the greater the potential for local food production.

3. DEVELOP AND ENCOURAGE LOCAL FOOD PRODUCTION

Cities can decrease their food supply vulnerability and lower the cost of their food by:

a. Making publicly-owned lands that are suitable for food production available for community gardens.
b. Providing local tax incentives for home/community produced food.
c. Establishing Urban Agricultural testing programs with the state Cooperative Extension Service to test crop varieties, analyze soil for nutrients and pollutants, test crops for pollutant residues, prepare demonstration sites for various types of urban agriculture and waste recycling and offer technical assistance on farming as well as design and construction of community greenhouses, cold frames, rooftop gardens, etc.
d. Facilitating long-term leasing of vacant lots to com-

munity groups for urban gardening and providing basic site improvement.

e. Establishing city-run gardens for low income individuals receiving food stamps to supplement their food allotment or providing seeds, access to land, tools and technical assistance as part of food stamp benefits.

f. Subsidizing gardens, or giving start-up funds to establish gardens and/or greenhouses, in schools, prisons, hospitals and nursing homes.

g. Developing loan funds for food self-reliance projects such as greenhouses, food preservation and storage operations, and small businesses associated with urban agriculture.

h. Establishing community farms on their urban fringes to be worked by local farmers.

i. Encouraging city agencies, as well as consumer groups, senior citizen and day care centers, hospitals, schools and prisons to purchase food directly from local farmers and processors.

j. Promoting contract growing (as practiced in Japan) whereby groups of urban families, or co-ops, or even the city itself, arranges to buy food directly from a local supplier.

k. Encouraging local industries which produce waste heat to make use of this energy by constructing greenhouses.

l. Establishing large-scale composting operations (such as the Bronx Frontier Development Corporation compost project in New York City) to turn vegetable, manure and other organic wastes into compost for urban gardens.

4. DEVELOP AND ENCOURAGE LOCAL MARKETS

Cities can increase the security and economy of their food supply and develop and encourage local markets by:

a. Encouraging and assisting the establishment of farmers' markets in the city, particularly in low-income neighborhoods, and facilitating authorizations for farmers to accept food stamps at the markets.

b. Helping establish mobile farmers' markets and/or fish markets to visit housing projects, neighborhood centers, apartment complexes and factories.

c. Assisting in the formation of buying clubs, food cooperatives, co-op stores and preservation/storage centers.

d. Providing incentives for supermarkets to remain in inner cities.

5. DEVELOP AND ENCOURAGE LOCAL FOOD PROCESSING AND STORAGE

Cities can increase the security of their food supply and develop and encourage local food processing and storage by:

a. Sponsoring community canning facilities where residents can preserve food inexpensively or free of charge.
b. Providing incentives to grocery stores to establish canning facilities for their shoppers.

6. FACILITATE ACCESS TO FOOD

Cities can insure that all segments of their population have a supply of food by:

a. Facilitating access to food stamps, emergency food outlets, and elderly feeding programs for those in need of these services.
b. Providing transportation to farmers' markets and "pick-your-own" operations.
c. Establishing a "Food and Hunger Hotline," (as is in operation in New York City) to provide referrals for emergency food, food stamps, elderly feeding sites, etc.

7. EDUCATE PEOPLE ABOUT THEIR FOOD SITUATION

Cities can increase the public's understanding of the food situation in the U.S., their state and city, and help people shop more economically by:

a. Organizing public meetings and/or educational programs explaining the importance of agriculture to urban areas, as well as offering classes in urban agriculture, aquaculture, container and rooftop gardening, food preservation, storage, and preparation, and nutrition. Wise food selection based on locally-produced foods should be taught in all classes.
b. Encouraging public schools to include classes on local/urban agriculture.

The path The Cornucopia Project sees as leading the individual states to a secure, sustainable and economical food supply, and as strengthening the entire U.S. food system, has the following dimensions:

Recommendations — States

1. REGIONALIZE THEIR FOOD SUPPLY

States can regionalize their food supply or increase their degree of self-reliance in basic food stuffs by taking steps to promote agricultural production within their own state boundaries, and in adjacent or nearby states by:

a. Diversifying production within their state by, for example, providing technical assistance from extension agents, and low-interest state-guaranteed loans for the changes necessary for diversification.

b. Mandating a study by each State Department of Agriculture and the state land grant university of the potential for producing the various crops needed in the state.

c. Establishing demonstration experiments to test crop, animal, and fish varieties suited to the state's soil and climate, and develop and test low input, sustainable farming techniques suitable to the state.

d. Providing incentives for farmers to diversify.

e. Providing tax incentives for small-scale food producers — such as not taxing the first $10,000 of income from food produced for local consumption.

f. Issuing state tax credits for home production, processing and storing of food.

g. Developing incentives to enter farming, such as guaranteed state loans with deferred or reduced payment until 5 years after start-up (as currently being done in Minnesota). States could also provide technical, managerial and organizational assistance for new farmers.

These efforts would not only strengthen the local food supply, they would enhance the local economy as well.

2. EXPAND LOCAL MARKETS

States can help expand markets to assure farmers of local outlets for their products by:

a. Establishing more farmers markets, especially in urban areas, and setting-up wholesale farmers markets, to supply retailers, consumer co-ops and other volume purchasers.

b. Giving preference to in-state producers in bidding for the sale of foods to state-run institutions.

c. Assisting farmers in establishing producer co-ops to facilitate bulk buying of supplies and services by volume purchasers.
d. Providing incentives for farmers to operate roadside stands and "pick-your-own" operations.
e. Establishing "good samaritan" laws whereby farmers are not held responsible for claims arising from the "gleaning" (clean-up of fields after machines or professional pickers have finished) of their fields.
f. Facilitating and promoting direct purchase of food from farmers by supermarkets, schools, hospitals, day care centers, senior citizen centers, company cafeterias, restaurants, etc.
g. Encouraging and providing assistance to processing plants that purchase local products.
h. Providing assistance to small growers through a statewide marketing clearinghouse.
i. Beginning or enhancing promotional campaigns (with specific logo to identify state-produced foods) to heighten awareness of the importance of local agriculture to the economy of the state and its residents.

3. PRESERVE FARMLAND

States can stop the loss of their farmland and protect their production potential by:

a. Instituting (or accelerating) the computerized mapping of farmland that is to be protected from development (as California has done).
b. Implementing modifications of farmland tax assessments to reflect current use value rather than potential market value.
c. Instituting programs for "Purchase of Development Rights," whereby a farmer who sells his development rights is paid the difference between the value of his acreage for development and its value for agriculture, thus keeping the land available for crops (as is being done in Suffolk County, New York).
d. Designating that class I and II lands be used for agricultural purposes only.[3]
e. Levying heavy taxes on profits made on the development of previously prime agricultural land.
f. Establishing agricultural districts (as is being done in New York) to protect farmland from urban expansion.
g. Acting to prevent "leapfrog" or random development, which

forces farmers to pay a disproportionate share of the new tax burden as urbanization creeps towards their farms.

h. Developing a procedure that allows the state "first refusal" rights to agricultural land being sold (as is done in France).

i. Providing tax incentives for farmers who voluntarily restrict development of their prime agricultural lands.

j. Instituting a farmland capital gains tax high enough to remove prime agricultural land from speculative markets.

4. STOP EROSION

States can stop or reverse the loss of their topsoil by:

a. Enforcing existing anti-erosion laws.

b. Establishing new penalties for erosion damage such as prohibiting all agricultural production activities which result in more than five tons of soil loss per acre per year—the maximum rate at which the soil's fertility can be maintained. And establishing rewards for soil enrichment, such as tax credits for on-farm soil and water conservation programs, including contour tillage, minimum tillage, and crop rotation.

c. Instituting and enforcing laws that require a conservation plan for all agricultural lands in excess of 25 acres.

d. Linking economic programs—such as loans, crop insurance, disaster relief, and state purchase of farm commodities—to avoidance of excessive soil erosion.

e. Instituting and enforcing a "severance tax" on soil losses due to excessive erosion. Tax revenues from farms permitting rapid erosion could be used to finance subsidies to encourage conservation practices, and to pay for downstream dredging of silt, damage to water treatment facilities and other social costs.

f. Using public subsidies, such as low interest loans, preferential farm property tax formulas and valuations and other tax incentives to encourage regional organic waste recycling, cover and permanent cropping, minimum tillage, ridge planting, proper rotation, longer rotations, biological nitrogen fixation, contour plowing, terracing, stripcropping, leaving harvest residues on soil surfaces, reducing soil compaction and salinity, and intercropping.

g. Developing incentives for encouraging the use of rental arrangements which include provisions for sharing erosion control and soil enrichment costs with landowner.

h. Developing public awareness programs to promote understanding of the need to support sound soil conservation practices.

i. Using performance contracts which tax farmers on their average tons of soil lost per acre per year.

Taking these actions would result in a drastic reduction in soil loss. According to the USDA, practicing *just* minimum tillage techniques on 80 percent of all U.S. cropland would reduce soil erosion by 50 percent or more.[4] In fact, the USDA reports that "the organic matter content of some soils has actually increased by 12 to 25 percent after 5 to 10 years of no-till cropping where tillage was previously done with a mold board plow."[5] The use of all available conservation techniques would not only stop the trend towards soil oblivion but reverse it. In parts of Europe, Japan and China, soil quality is better now than it was thousands of years ago when farming first began.

Imposing soil loss restrictions would not add appreciably to the cost of food. One study found that cutting Iowa's soil loss 75 to 90 percent would only increase the per-capita cost of producing food and fiber by about 4 percent.[6] In addition, reservoir siltation and dredging costs would decrease, and the savings could finance many soil enrichment programs. Pollution from fertilizer and pesticide runoff would also be greatly reduced.

By stopping soil erosion, and conserving and enriching the soils,

—the U.S. would clean its streams, rivers, and lakes of their largest pollutants,
—drastically reduce toxic run-offs,
—reduce dredging costs,
—expand reservoir longevity,
—maintain and increase farm productivity,
—decrease wind blown soil damage,
—reduce inflation caused by the need for ever higher-priced fertilizers and pesticides to maintain soil productivity,
—cut on-farm energy use by making soils lighter and easier to plow,
—improve soil fertility,
—reduce drought damage by improving soil structure and water-holding capacity, and,
—increase the esthetic beauty of the entire landscape.

The annual U.S. soil loss cost of $6 to 57 billion could be greatly reduced, and possibly reversed. By building up our soils instead of washing them down the river, we will be building equity. Topsoils that don't wash away in 1982 will add to crop yields in 1983. Policies are needed that translate this long-term equity into short-term dollar gain so that the farmer is financially rewarded for soil enrichment (and other sustainable agricultural techniques), not punished as he is in today's short-sighted economic accounting system.

5. DEVELOP ON-FARM RENEWABLE ENERGY SOURCES

States can encourage food producers and processors to switch from depletable to non-depletable types of energy, freeing them from the threat of shortages and escalating prices of these inputs, and creating a more stable, adaptive, and anti-inflationary food system. Decreasing the overall demand for oil will improve the U.S.'s balance-of-payments situation, and minimize the environmental impact of present day energy-intensive practices.

In the next 10 years, the U.S. food system will spend at least $400 billion just for the non-renewable fuels to provide us with food.[7] This figure does *not* include increases caused by inflation, or price jumps due to international factors or increases in demand. With such items, the figure could easily be doubled.

To switch the energy base of the U.S. food system from non-renewable to renewable energy will be expensive, but to continue to run the food system almost entirely on fossil fuels as we are now doing will be even more expensive. For example, to produce the amount of energy currently consumed by the U.S. food system with present solar energy technology would cost about $500 billion.[7] But once the system was switched over to renewable energy, the annual costs for fuel would be greatly reduced, and the annual costs for imported oil (a major driving force behind inflation) would be eliminated.

States can help bring about a transition from depletable to renewable energy sources by:

a. Conducting regional inventories of all renewable energy sources.

b. Providing incentives, such as tax credits for investments made in agricultural energy conservation and on-site development of renewable energy sources; or low-interest loans for accomplishing the same; or tax exemptions for income received from the production of renewable energy.

c. Setting up pilot projects and demonstration sites using alternative forms of energy for various types of farms, and showing recycling and the use of sludge.

6. CONSERVE WATER

States can help insure that they will have water for farming, industry, commerce and consumers by:

a. Pricing water to more accurately reflect its actual costs. For example, farmers in the Central Valley in California pay $3.50 an acre-foot for their irrigation water. Without subsidies, the cost of this water would be $1,100 per acre-foot. And if aquifers become exhausted, the price would be astronomical.

b. Eliminating the use of declining block rate structures, whereby the largest user of water gets charged the lowest rate. Instead, flat-rates, inclining block rates, where the heaviest users have the highest rates, or seasonal rates can be instituted.

c. Providing investment incentives for drip irrigation and other water conservation equipment.

7. RECYCLE ORGANIC WASTES

States can increase the efficiency of their food system by:

a. Preparing a state-wide inventory of the types and amounts of organic wastes available now and in the future and assess the ability of these wastes to improve soil fertility and tilth.

b. Establishing an Agricultural Waste Council in their State Department of Agriculture to develop desirable legislation and other measures to facilitate recycling of wastes.

c. Developing incentives for using local organic wastes for fertilizer and incentives to industry to separate toxic substances from their wastes so that it might be more safely used on cropland.

d. Setting up pilot projects and demonstration sites for recycling and the use of sludge.

8. DEVELOP IN-STATE FOOD PROCESSING

States can stop the loss of their food processing industries and improve processing capabilities by:

a. Providing incentives for existing food companies to develop more energy-efficient processing and packaging techniques, along with incentives to attract new food processors who wish to reduce transportation costs by locating near a major distribution center. Developing a food processing industry which meets the needs of producers and consumers within the local economy will enhance the entire state economy.

   b. Providing incentives for on-farm processing, cooling and fresh packing of local food crops.

   c. Helping establish community food processing and storage facilities for the use of families and small commercial food producers. In this way, economies in equipment and energy consumption can be realized.

   d. Developing incentives for expanding their livestock slaughtering and storage facilities.

9. DEVELOP LONG-RANGE FOOD SYSTEM PLANS

States can begin to deal with the growing complexities and vulnerabilities of their food supply by:

   a. Developing an overall state food policy which will increase regional self-reliance and economic viability while decreasing the vulnerability of the state's food supply.

   b. Developing an emergency food plan to deal with a food supply disruption. This might provide for regional grain storage facilities and the formation of state-wide communication and coordination centers.

   c. Conducting an annual study of the condition of the state food system that will illustrate the amount of food currently being imported and exported, the amount of land lost to development, soil erosion losses, and what measures need to be taken to increase the state's self-reliance.

10. INITIATE EDUCATION PROGRAMS

States can help farmers, consumers, cities, and food industry leaders be aware of the options available to them by:

   a. Developing consumer education programs to increase awareness of locally grown produce.

   b. Initiating educational programs on farmland preservation, farm energy conservation, reduced pesticide and fertilizer use, recycling of organic wastes, and energy expenditures in different methods of farming and home food production and preparation.

   c. Promoting nutrition education campaigns to illustrate the relationships between diet and health, and the benefits of fresh, seasonal, locally-grown and minimally processed foods, as well as bulk purchasing of food.

d. Communicating the goals and the condition of the state's food system as revealed in their annual study. (See 9.c.)

11. REVITALIZE FISHING INDUSTRY

States can help in revitalizing their fishing industry by:

a. Developing more direct marketing systems, including inland market options for surpluses.

b. Participating with other states and the Federal Government in keeping annual harvests below best estimates of maximum sustainable yield for all species.

c. Enacting and enforcing stricter laws regulating dumping of pollutants in marine waters.

d. Providing investment incentives for aquaculture within the state.

12. ENHANCE CONSUMER AND ENVIRONMENTAL SAFETY

States can protect their citizens and their natural environment by:

a. Strictly enforcing existing environmental protection laws.

b. Developing programs for safer handling of toxic pesticides and stronger enforcement of laws against pesticide misuse— such as spray drift and farmworker exposure to newly sprayed fields.

c. Developing stricter standards for pesticide residues in foods.

The path The Cornucopia Project sees as leading the entire United States to a secure, economical, and sustainable food system, and as enhancing the welfare of all the world's people, has the following dimensions:

Recommendations — Federal Level

1. ELIMINATE SUBSIDIES TO NON-SUSTAINABLE AGRICULTURE

U.S. tax laws and other subsidies can be changed to favor sustainable agriculture by:

a. Eliminating well-water depletion allowances that encourage pumping water at rates which exhaust the underlying aquifer.

b. Eliminating tax laws that encourage the purchase of new,

larger, and more expensive farm machinery, thereby pushing the farmer deeper in debt and increasing soil compaction.

c. Eliminating tax laws that encourage the accumulation of huge debts.

d. Eliminating tax laws that encourage land speculation and absentee ownership of farmland. With present-day arrangements, favorable taxes and steadily rising land prices encourage individuals and businesses to buy farmland as an investment and hedge against inflation rather than as a primary means of earning a livelihood.

e. Eliminating the export of subsidized grain, or grain sold below production cost.

f. Eliminating or vastly reducing research and development funds for non-sustainable agriculture.

g. Modifying Agricultural Stabilization and Conservation Service regulations for cost-sharing programs so that farmers who use organic techniques can participate. Currently, in order to qualify for certain tillage, seed, lime and permanent pasture programs, farmers must apply particular commercial fertilizers based on mandatory soil test results. This commercial fertilizer requirement should be changed so that equivalent organic fertilizers may be substituted.

h. Modifying current USDA commodity stabilization programs that regulate cropland acreage to establish a category of cropland called "voluntarily diverted cropland" that would recognize any land that the farmer converts from crops to grass or trees. If this land were recognized as a part of the farmer's cropland base, when commodity circumstances call for reduced planting of certain crops, farmers would not be penalized for seeking to conserve their soils (as they are now).

i. Removing all production subsidies to tobacco, a proven carcinogen.

2. DEVELOP A LONG RANGE NATIONAL FOOD PLAN

The U.S. can develop a comprehensive food plan. Many of the problems plaguing our food system result from the lack of an explicit long-range food plan. The question of where the food system should be in 20 years is not addressed in any meaningful sense. Crop projections for the next year are the usual time horizon for much of what happens with the U.S. food production system. We need to do better. Goals and strategies for reaching a sustainable food system need to developed and explicitly stated.

3. DEVELOP REGIONAL FOOD SYSTEMS

The U.S. can work toward a regional food system. Every region (every group of states, each state, and subregions within each state) has a unique climate, geology, soil, demography, economy, resource base and culture. Each has its own particular food needs. By encouraging different regions to become more self-reliant and self-sufficient in food production,

- —the whole national system can become more stable and adaptable,
- —energy use can be cut back through decreased transportation,
- —costs can be reduced because of lower transportation and processing needs,
- —more fresh and nutritional food can be consumed,
- —local waste can be recycled onto farmlands, reducing synthetic fertilizer needs and increasing soil health,
- —more jobs can be created in the region, and
- —the local economy can become more stable and vital.

Regionalization is not a step backwards in time to a period when the U.S. actually was a series of self-sufficient and self-reliant groups of regions, but rather is a step forward into the vastly more complex world of the future. It is a way of learning from the past, like the use of modern wind turbines by U.S. utilities to generate electricity. Increased regional self-reliance is not a call for decreasing adaptability, or a return to an over-romanticized bygone era, but rather an effort to increase each region's capability to provide for its own needs.

Just as America's older industries need to be revitalized and "reindustrialized", to make them more efficient and in tune with present economic realities, America's oldest industry—the food system—needs to be regenerated into a more efficient and sustainable system. The technology that allowed the development of the vast global inter-linkages that are the hallmark of today's food system need to be "miniaturized" and made appropriate for local regions. The know-how that makes it possible for "inexpensive" California lettuce to be sold in New York needs to be applied to the production and sale of even less-expensive New York lettuce. And what food must be shipped long distances—possibly wheat, bananas, citrus fruits, etc.—needs to be moved more efficiently.

The Federal government can help increase regional food self-reliance by:

a. Developing a federal food policy that facilitates state, city, consumer, farmer and industry programs for dealing with soil and land conservation, energy conservation, regional food systems, and sustainable agriculture. Part of the overall food policy can be an emergency plan to deal with a disruption in national food supply.

b. Providing funds for the development of regional and state food system inventories and "firstcut" transitional plans to more self-reliant state food systems.

c. Decentralizing certain parts of the U.S. Department of Agriculture. By giving each state Department of Agriculture more control over its land grant universities, research funds, extension agents, loan funds, soil conservation service, etc. the individual states will be better equipped to develop a regional and sustainable food system tailored to their unique needs.

d. Giving preference to local producers for Federal food purchases for the armed forces, hospitals, offices, schools, etc. This could save about $4 billion per year in transportation costs for U.S. taxpayers.[8a]

e. Eliminating or reducing federal subsidies for long distance food transportation. For example, trucks do not pay their share of highway maintenance. This amounts to a subsidy to the trucking of food across the country. If trucks had to pay for the damage they do to the nation's highways, long distance transport of food would be very expensive.

One way of reducing the subsidy to long distance food shipment would be to add the hidden costs, currently borne by U.S. taxpayers, directly to the cost of gasoline and diesel fuel in the form of an additional federal tax. This type of arrangement would charge all transportation costs directly to transportation users.

At present, only 65 percent of highway maintenance and construction costs are charged directly to users. A $10.8 billion annual government subsidy covers the remainder of the costs. If this subsidy was allocated to the 125 billion gallons of transportation fuel consumed annually, it would result in an increase of $.09 per gallon.

Economic losses due to highway accidents could also be allocated in the same way. These losses total over $56.4 billion annually. If collected through a gasoline tax, they would add an additional $.45 to the cost of each gallon of gasoline.

In addition, about one-half of all air pollution in this country is from road vehicles. Thus, $275 million (one-half of the $543 million spent each year for air quality control programs) could be added to the cost of gasoline. Together, these three hidden costs would add $.55 to the price of each gallon of gasoline, an increase to 50 percent in fuel costs.[9]

f. Placing limits on the amount of price support or payments which any one farmer can receive. That would help reverse the trend toward fewer and larger farms. Current commodity support programs reward landowners rather than farmers.

4. STOP SOIL EROSION AND PRESERVE FARMLAND

The federal government can emphasize that the privileges of land ownership are balanced by obligations and responsibilities. These include not only preventing one's land from eroding or preserving its nutrients, but also include the notion that land owners/trustees have an obligation to do something useful with their land; that social benefits flow from good land use and social costs result from idle or neglected land.[10]

The United States can act forcefully to reverse the loss of its topsoil and farmland by:

a. Declaring its remaining topsoil and farmland a national trust.
b. Developing strong incentives to reverse soil erosion, such as linking price support, loan guarantee and owner and operator loans to participation in soil conservation programs.
c. Developing Federal land-use policy guidelines that help local governments find ways to stop development of prime farmland.
d. Restricting Federal funding for development on prime farmland or using prime farmland only as a last resort in any Federal construction projects.
e. Using performance contracts which tax farmers on their average ton of soil loss per acre per year.
f. Not recognizing as cropland *any* new lands that do not meet the criteria for Capability Classes I through IV, and making programs such as crop insurance and disaster relief unavailable on lands that do not qualify as Class IV or better unless the farmer can demonstrate that he has applied an effective conservation system onto the land. Federal programs need to stop subsidizing the cultivation

of unsuited soils because the public gets stuck with paying three bills: the cost of the subsidy itself, the unfair competition this subsidized farmer has over the unsubsidized farmer, and the topsoil loss, water and air pollution, and related costs of soil erosion.

g. Recognizing or certifying farmers who are initiating, managing and maintaining conservation systems on their land. Each farmer that carried out a satisfactory conservation program would earn a "Green Ticket" that could be used to apply for special benefits under USDA's farm programs—such as reduced crop insurance premiums, and lower interest rates on loans from Farmers Home Administration and private lending institutions—since the conservation system provides assurance of continued levels of productivity.

Measured against the $6 to 57 billion annual loss of U.S. topsoil, the cost of these programs would more than justify themselves. It can be argued that we lose more dollars in soil loss each *year* than the $10 billion the United States has spent on erosion control programs since it began allocating money back in 1935.[11] Given the annual costs of soil loss, much greater expenditures are warranted.

5. FUND SUSTAINABLE FOOD SYSTEM RESEARCH

Federal research and development efforts can explore more effective and economical ways to make the switch from our present system of food production and distribution to sustainable systems by funding research in such areas as soil fertility, crop production, animal production, and transitional agriculture. Such research could help by:

a. Determining the impact on soil life and growth of different cultivation and rotation methods, including no-till, intercropping and monoculture, and different materials such as compost humates, seaweed, dolomitic lime, synthetic or acidulated fertilizers, seed and soil inoculants, acid rain, herbicides and pesticides.

b. Studying the effects of rotations and tillage practices on weed shifts, the effects of plant combinations and densities on pest management, and the holistic interactions of various cropping systems according to climatic zone, farm size, and type of farm.

c. Developing procedures to reduce anitibiotic and chemical use to control animal disease.

d. Determining transition rotations for small and large farms, comparing abrupt transitions to gradual changes, and finding ways for "cleansing" soil of toxic substances.

(For details in this area see The Cornucopia Project's report, "Research Agenda for the Transition to a Sustainable Agriculture".)

6. CHANGE GRADING AND MARKETING STANDARDS

Federal grading and marketing standards can be overhauled to eliminate outmoded incentives or subsidies by:

a. Allowing beef fed with a much higher percentage of grass or roughage to grade choice. (Current practices give a subsidy to the less efficient corn-fed beef.)
b. Modifying USDA marketing orders so that nutritional content of fruit and vegetables—and not just cosmetic appearance—is an indicator of product quality.
c. Requiring labels for all products to list the origin of that product. In this way, consumers will be able to know which products are from their locality.

7. FACILITATE LOCAL FOOD SYSTEMS

The federal government can facilitate the development of local food systems and increase national security and local economic viability by:

a. Providing federal tax incentives for home food production, including greenhouse and growframe construction.
b. Developing widespread home and urban gardening extension services to assist the 34 million American households with gardens.

8. HELP ELIMINATE GLOBAL FOOD INSECURITY

The United States can protect its citizens, help eliminate hunger, malnutrition and famine, reduce the growing disparity between the rich and poor countries, help stabilize international relations and provide the foundation for a durable peace by:

a. Establishing or participating in an international grain reserve for famine relief.
b. Helping food-short countries increase their self-reliance by providing appropriate technical and financial support in such areas as intensive, small-scale, sustainable food production, and local food storage.

c. Stopping the sale to foreign countries of pesticides banned or restricted in the United States. This will protect agricultural workers in these countries as well as stop the export of pesticide-poisoned crops to the United States by these same countries, with the resulting poisoning of U.S. citizens as well as citizens of other nations.

d. Participating in global efforts to protect fish stocks.

e. Stopping the export of the United States' limited supply of the strategically important phosphate fertilizer.

f. Instituting a 10 percent surcharge/tax on grain sold to developed countries as a means of financing an international grain reserve and paying for U.S. soil conservation efforts.

g. Decreasing our imports of forest products, thereby helping to preserve vital forests in developing parts of the world.

h. Increasing "user fees" paid by government-subsidized foreign fishing fleets in U.S. waters, thereby helping to insure a sustainable harvest.

SUMMARY

Recommendations—Farmers

1. REDUCE DEBT
2. DIVERSIFY PRODUCTION ENTERPRISE
3. STOP SOIL EROSION
4. EXPERIMENT WITH PERMANENT AGRICULTURE
5. CHANGE GRADING AND MARKETING STANDARDS
6. EXPLORE DIRECT RETAIL SALES
7. DEVELOP ON-FARM ALTERNATIVE ENERGY SOURCES
8. DEVELOP ON-FARM FERTILIZER SOURCES
9. SELL TO FOODSERVICE MARKETS

Recommendations—Consumers

1. INCREASE FOOD SYSTEM AWARENESS AND INVOLVEMENT
2. CONSUME FRESH, LOCALLY-GROWN FRUITS AND VEGETABLES
3. SUPPORT LOCAL FARMERS
4. DEVELOP PRUDENT DIET
5. GROW MORE
6. PROCESS AND PRESERVE MORE
7. EXTEND GROWING-SEASON
8. PRODUCE MEAT OR FISH

Recommendations—Food Industry

1. ENCOURAGE SUSTAINABLE FARMING METHODS

2. MINIMIZE ENERGY AND MATERIAL USE
3. REGIONALIZE FOOD PURCHASING, PROCESSING
   AND DISTRIBUTION
4. PROMOTE FRESH, LOCALLY-PRODUCED FOOD
5. WORK COOPERATIVELY WITH CONSUMERS
6. PROVIDE ADDITIONAL FOOD-RELATED SERVICES
7. DEVELOP NEEDED NEW PRODUCTS
8. SEE FOOD IN BROADER CONTEXT

Recommendations—Cities

1. ESTABLISH DEPARTMENT OF FOOD
2. PRESERVE FARMLAND
3. DEVELOP AND ENCOURAGE LOCAL FOOD PRODUCTION
4. DEVELOP AND ENCOURAGE LOCAL MARKETS
5. DEVELOP AND ENCOURAGE LOCAL FOOD PROCESSING
   AND STORAGE
6. FACILITATE ACCESS TO FOOD
7. EDUCATE POPULATION ABOUT FOOD SITUATION

Recommendations—States

1. REGIONALIZE THEIR FOOD SUPPLY
2. EXPAND LOCAL MARKETS
3. PRESERVE FARMLAND
4. STOP EROSION
5. DEVELOP ON-FARM RENEWABLE ENERGY SOURCES
6. CONSERVE WATER
7. RECYCLE ORGANIC WASTES
8. DEVELOP IN-STATE FOOD PROCESSING
9. DEVELOP LONG-RANGE FOOD SYSTEM PLANS
10. INITIATE EDUCATION PROGRAMS
11. REVITALIZE FISHING INDUSTRY
12. ENHANCE CONSUMER AND ENVIRONMENTAL SAFETY

Recommendations—Federal Level

1. ELIMINATE SUBSIDIES TO NON-SUSTAINABLE AGRICULTURE
2. DEVELOP LONG-RANGE NATIONAL FOOD PLAN
3. DEVELOP REGIONAL FOOD SYSTEMS
4. STOP SOIL EROSION AND PRESERVE FARMLAND
5. FUND SUSTAINABLE FOOD SYSTEM RESEARCH
6. CHANGE GRADING AND MARKETING STANDARDS
7. FACILITATE LOCAL FOOD SYSTEMS
8. HELP ELIMINATE GLOBAL FOOD INSECURITY

3
Summary/Conclusions

The preceding lists of recommendations are not easy reading. They will be harder to implement, but trying to pick up the pieces after a food system crash would be even harder, if not impossible.

Our recommendations should be viewed as a flexible agenda rather than a rigid program. They are what we know today. Tomorrow, as we learn more, we can revise our assessments of the problems and our options. We hope that part of *our* learning process will come from you, in the form of feedback on what you've read in this report.

It is vital that we all realize we have the option to change our food system. But it is just as important that we begin to exercise that option today.

4
Notes:

The Success of the U.S. Food System

1. U.S., Department of Agriculture, *Agricultural Statistics 1980* (Washington, D.C.: Government Printing Office, 1980), p. 429.
2. S.H. Wittwer, "Food Production: Technology and the Resource Base," *Science*, 188, No. 4188 (1975), p. 579.
3. U.S., Department of Agriculture, *Agricultural Statistics*, p. 443.
4. *National Food Review*, Economics and Statistics Service, U.S., Department of Agriculture, Spring 1981, NFR-14, p. 2.
5. U.S., Department of Commerce, Bureau of the Census, *Statistical Abstract of the United States*, 1980. 101st ed. (Washington, D.C.: Government Printing Office, 1980), p. 414.
6. Penelope C. Cate, *U.S. Agricultural Exports*, Food and Agriculture Section, Environment and Natural Resources Policy Division, The Library of Congress (Washington, D.C.: Congressional Research Service, 1981), p. 1.
7. U.S., Department of Commerce, *Statistical Abstract 1980*, p. 625.
8. U.S., Department of Agriculture, *Agricultural Statistics 1980*, p. 443.
9. "Food Takes Smaller Bite from U.S. Pocketbooks," *Allentown Morning Call*, December 16, 1980.
10. Roger Burbach and Patricia Flynn, *Agribusiness in the Americas* (New York: Monthly Review Press, 1980), p. 64.
11. William Serrin, "New York Area's Reliance on Imported Food Grows," *New York Times*, July 26, 1981.
12. Calculation based on populations of: Maine, New Hampshire, Vermont, Connecticut, Massachusetts, Rhode Island, New York, New Jersey, Delaware, Maryland, Washington, D.C., Virginia,
128

West Virginia, *(Statistical Abstract of The United States,* p. 12.)
   population = 62,000,000
Per capita consumption of food per year = 1,463 lbs. *(Agricultural Statistics, 1980,* p. 554)
   $(62 \times 10^6) \times 1,463 = 90,706,000,000$ lbs. food consumed.
   $90,706,000,000 \times 80\%$ (amount of food imported) =
   72,564,800,000 lbs.
   $72,564,800,000 \div 52 = 1,395,476,923$ lbs. per week
   $1,395,476,923 \div 40,000 = 34,886$ trucks per week

13. *The Pennsylvania Food System: Crash or Self-Reliance?*
    Report by The Cornucopia Project (Emmaus: Rodale Press,
    1981), p. 9.
14. U.S., Department of Energy, *Agriculture and Food Processes
    Branch Program Summary Document,* (Springfield: National
    Technical Information Service, 1980), p. 12.
15. Remarks by Walter Heller, Director of Research, *Progressive
    Grocer Magazine,* at the Annual Meeting of the Association
    for Dressings and Sauces, October 26, 1981.
16. U.S., Department of Agriculture, *1979 Book of Agricultural
    Charts,* Agricultural Handbook No. 561, (Washington, D.C.:
    Government Printing Office, 1979), p. 10.
17. Jack Markowitz, "Food Imports, Supply Disruptions Could Leave
    State Hungry," *Pennsylvania Economy* 1, No. 11 (1981), p. 2.

Economic Structure

1. U.S., Department of Agriculture, *1979 Handbook of Agricultural Charts,* Agricultural Handbook, No.561, (Washington,
   D.C.: Government Printing Office), p. 29.
   U.S., Department of Agriculture, *Agricultural Statistics 1980,*
   (Washington, D.C.: Government Printing Office), 1980, pp.
   417, 418.
2. U.S., General Accounting Office, *Food, Agriculture, and Nutrition Issues for Planning,* (Washington, D.C.: Government
   Printing Office, June 11, 1980), p. 32.
3. Bob Bergland, "It's Time to Rethink Our Farm Policy," *Country
   Journal,* November 1979, p. 48.
4. U.S., Department of Agriculture, *1979 Handbook of Agricultural Charts,* Agriculture Handbook No. 561, (Washington,
   D.C.: Government Printing Office, October 1979), p. 7.
5. T.A. Miller, G.E. Rodewald and R.G. McElroy, *Economies of Size
   in U.S. Field Crop Farming,* U.S., Department of Agriculture,
   Economics and Statistics Service, Agricultural Economic Report

No. 472, (Washington, D.C.: Government Printing Office, July 1981).

U.S., Department of Agriculture, *A Time to Choose: Summary Report on the Structure of Agriculture*, (Washington, D.C.: Government Printing Office, January 1981), pp. 57-59.

6. U.S., Department of Agriculture, *1979 Handbook of Agricultural Charts*, op. cit., p. 29.

   U.S., Department of Agriculture, *Agricultural Statistics 1980*, op. cit., pp. 417, 418.

7. U.S., Department of Agriculture, *A Time to Choose: Summary Report on the Structure of Agriculture*, op. cit., p. 74.

8. Thomas McDonald and George Coffman, *Fewer, Larger U.S. Farms, by Year 2000—and Some Consequences*, U.S., Department of Agriculture, Economics and Statistics Service, Agriculture Information Bulletin No. 439, (Washington, D.C.: Government Printing Office, October, 1980), p. 8.

9. Jack Doyle, Testimony before the subcommittee on Forests, Family Farms and Energy of the Committee on Agriculture, U.S. House of Representatives, March 2, 1981, p. 17.

10. Bob Bergland, op. cit., p. 48.

11. Ibid., p. 49.

12. Stanley D. Schiff, "Land and Food: Dilemmas in Protecting the Resource Base," *Journal of Soil and Water Conservation*, March/April 1979, Vol. 34, #2, p. 55.

13. Marc Reisner, "The Irony of The Blooming Desert," *APF Reporter*, June 1979, Vol. 2, #4, p. 8.

14. U.S., Department of Agriculture, *Agricultural Statistics 1980*, (Washington, D.C.: Government Printing Office), pp. 477, 483.

    U.S., Department of Agriculture, *1979 Handbook of Agricultural Charts*, Agricultural Handbook No. 561, (Washington, D.C.: Government Printing Office), p. 10, chart 12.

15. U.S., Department of Agriculture, *Agricultural Statistics 1980*, (Washington, D.C.: Government Printing Office, 1980), p. 417.

    $160 billion ÷ 2.3 million (# of farms in U.S.) = $69,600/farm.

16. U.S., Department of Agriculture, *A Time to Choose: Summary Report on the Structure of Agriculture*, op. cit., p. 114.

17. U.S., Department of Agriculture, *1980 Handbook of Agricultural Charts*, Agricultural Handbook No. 574, (Washington, D.C.: Government Printing Office, October 1980), p. 11.

18. Gene Logsdon and Jim Ritchie, "Can the Family Farms Survive the Eighties? Decade of Decision," *The New Farm*, January 1981, Vol. 3, #1, pp. 46-51, (Interview with Harold Breimyer).

19. U.S., Department of Agriculture, *Fact Book of U.S. Agriculture,* Miscellaneous Publication, Number 1063, (Washington, D.C.: Government Printing Office, November 1980), p. 14.
20. "Replacing Energy As The Inflation Villain." *Business Week,* June 1, 1981, p. 73.
21. Don Paarlberg, *Farm and Food Policy, Issues of the 1980's,* (Lincoln, Nebraska: University of Nebraska Press, 1980), p. 184.
22. Frank Press, "Science and Technology: The Road Ahead," *Science,* Vol. 200, May 19, 1978, p. 739.
23. Anthony E. Gallo, "Food Spending and Income," *National Food Review,* United States Department of Agriculture, Economics and Statistics Service, Spring, 1981, p. 2.
24. U.S., Department of Agriculture, *National Food Review,* Economics and Statistics Service, Winter, 1981, p. 4.
25. "Food Takes Smaller Bite from U.S. Pocketbooks," *Allentown Morning Call,* December 16, 1980.
26. Anthony E. Gallo, op. cit.
27. *Directory of U.S. Food Plants,* (Radnor, Pennsylvania: Chilton's Food Engineering, 1981).
28. Jack Doyle, Testimony before the Subcommittee on Forests, Family Farms and Energy, of the Committee on Agriculture, U.S. House of Representatives, March 2, 1981, p. 17.
29. "Grocery Industry Report for 1980," *Progressive Grocer,* Vol. 60, No. 4, April 1981, p. 43.
30. A.V. Krebs, *1976 Directory of Major U.S. Corporations Involved in Agribusiness,* (San Francisco: Agribusiness Accountability Project, 1976), p. 3.
31. William Serrin, "Let Them Eat Junk," *Saturday Review,* Vol. 7, No. 3, February 2, 1980, p. 20.
32. "Borden Cheese: It Could Make a Cow Cry," *New York Times,* Business Section, September 27, 1981, p. 21.
33. Donald Janson, "Campbell Likes Jersey, Not Its Tomato," *New York Times,* October 27, 1979.
34. Fred Strebeigh, "Potentials," *Quest/81,* June, 1981, p. 57.
35. Daniel Zwerdling, "The Food Monsters," *The Progressive,* Vol. 44, No. 3, March 1980, p. 25.
36. Anthony E. Gallo, John M. Connor, and William T. Boehm, "Mass Media Food Advertising," *National Food Review,* Winter, 1980, p. 10.
37. Anthony E. Gallo, "Food Advertising," *National Food Review,* Winter, 1981, pp. 7, 10.
38. Ibid., p. 10.

39. Henry J. Frundt, "Four Food Strategies," *Agribusiness Manual,* Interfaith Center on Corporate Responsibility, p. IV-4.
40. Robert C. Baker, "The Problem of Food Waste," *New York's Food and Life Sciences,* Vol. 11, No. 2, 1978, p. 23.

Food Transport

1. U.S., Bureau of the Census, *Statistical Abstract of the United States, 1980,* 101st ed. (Washington, D.C.: Government Printing Office, 1981), p. 643.
2. Douglas E. Bowers, "Transportation Technology and Agriculture in Twentieth Century America," *Journal of NAL Associates,* 5, No. 12, January/June (1980).
3. U.S., Bureau of the Census, *Statistical Abstract,* pp. 636, 642, 651, 653, 765.
4. U.S., Department of Agriculture, *1980 Handbook of Agricultural Charts,* Agricultural Handbook No. 574, (Washington, D.C.: Government Printing Office, 1980), p. 39. Food expenditures in 1979 (excluding alcoholic beverages) = $267.9 billion (*Statistical Abstract* p. 442).
    267.9 billion $\times$ .053 = 14,198,700,000.
5. U.S., Department of Defense, *U.S. Agriculture: Potential Vulnerabilities,* Research Report Prepared by the Stanford Research Institute, Menlo Park, California, January, 1969, p. 74.
6. Bowers, op. cit., p. 16.
7. American Trucking Associations, Inc., *American Trucking Trends 1977-1978* (Washington, D.C.: American Trucking Association, 1979), pp. 27, 28.
8. U.S., Department of Agriculture, "Spotlight on Refrigerated Rail Shipments," *Agricultural Outlook,* September, 1981, p. 17.
9. Walter Vergara, "Toward Optimization of Energy Consumption in Food Distribution," Proceedings of the Northeast Agricultural Leadership Assembly, Vol. 2, March 10-22, 1979, Cherry Hill, New Jersey, p. 257.
10. Figure on fuel costs for trucks taken from interview with T.Q. Hutchinson of the Transportation Division of the USDA.
11. U.S., Department of Agriculture, "Spotlight on Refrigerated Rail Shipments," p. 16.
12. 1977 Census of Transportation.
13. U.S., Department of Agriculture, "Spotlight on Refrigerated Rail Shipments," p. 16.
14. Ibid.

15. 1977 Census of Transportation: *Truck Inventory, and Use Survey* (Washington, D.C.: Government Printing Office, 1980), p. 40. Total trucks (by major use) used by agriculture, manufacturing, wholesale trade, retail trade, for-hire, services, used primarily to haul products, live animals and processed foods.
16. Ibid., p. 48. Total truck miles used by agriculture, manufacturing, wholesale trade, retail trade, for-hire, services, used primarily to haul farm products, live animals, processed foods.
17. U.S. Bureau of the Census, *Statistical Abstract*, p. 659. Total truck miles In 1977 (excluding truck miles for personal transportation) = 169,100,000,000.
18. Ibid., p. 653. Total consumption of motor fuels (1978) = 1.25 × 10^{11} gallons. Fuel consumption by trucks = 45,180 million truck miles ÷ 8.68 mpg = 5.205 × 10^9 gallons.
19. 5,205,057,604 gallons × $1.06 per gallon (1981 diesel fuel price).
20. U.S. Bureau of the Census, *Statistical Abstract*, p. 217. Air pollution due to road vehicles = 94.82 million tons (1978), trucks carrying food consume 4.35 percent of total motor fuel used in 1978. 94.82 million tons × .0435 = 4,124,670 tons of pollutants from trucks carrying food.
21. American Trucking Associations, p. 26.
22. Report by the Comptroller General, *Excessive Truck Weight: An Expensive Burden We Can No Longer Bear* (Washington, D.C.: Government Printing Office, 1979), p. 62.
23. Suzanne Rogalin, "High Costs on the Highways: Can We Afford to Keep on Truckin'?" *Cry California*, Vol. 3, No. 3, Summer (1978), pp. 18-22.
24. *Food Losses and Wastes in the Domestic Food Chain of the United States*, Final Report for Research Applied to National Needs, Research at Michigan State University (n.p. DAR 76-80693, 1979), p. 348.
25. "Out of Trucks, Out of Luck," *American Vegetable Grower*, 27, No. 8, August (1978), p. 8.

Land Use/Soil Abuse

1. U.S., Department of Agriculture, *1980 Appraisal, Part I, Soil, Water, and Related Resources in the United States, Condition, and Trends* (Washington, D.C.: Government Printing Office, 1981), p. 101. This figure represents soil loss from all *non-federal* cropland, pastureland, forestland, and rangeland, due to sheet, rill and wind erosion, and erosion from streambanks, gullies, roads and roadsides, and construction sites.

2. 6.4 billion tons of soil are eroded annually. 160 tons of topsoil will cover 1 acre to a depth of 1 inch (160 tons/acre/inch). $(6.4 \times 10^9) \div 160 = 40 \times 10^6$ acres/inch. Total cropland for Maine, New Hampshire, Vermont, Massachusetts, Connecticut, Rhode Island, New York, New Jersey, Pennsylvania, Delaware, Maryland, Alabama, Arizona, California and Florida = 35,989,000 acres (USDA Soil Conservation Service, Basis Statistics 1977 *National Resources Inventory*, rev 1980, table 3).

   There are 34,900 supermarkets in the United States, each having an average area of 20,000 sq. ft. (Food Marketing Institute, Information Services, Washington, D.C.) $34,900 \times 20,000 = 698 \times 10^6$ total sq. ft.

   6.4 billion tons of soil = 40,000,000 acres or $1,742,400 \times 10^6$ $(1,742,400 \times 10^6) \div (698 \times 10^6) = 2,496.275$ inches $\div 12 = 208$ ft. of soil atop every supermarket in the United States.

3. Neil Sampson, "The Ethical Dimension of Farmland Protection," *Farmland, Food and the Future* (Ankeny: Soil Conservation Society of American, 1979), p. 93.

4. U.S., Department of Agriculture, *1980 Appraisal, Part I*, p. 101.

5. U.S. Department of Agriculture Conservation Service, *Basic Statistics 1977 National Resources Inventory*, rev. 1980 (Washington, D.C.: Soil Conservation Service, 1980), table 16.

6. U.S., Department of Agriculture Soil Conservation Service, *America's Soil and Water: Condition and Trends* (Washington, D.C.: Government Printing Office, 1980), p. 8.

7. Ibid., p. 9.

8. "Learning From the Past," *Agricultural Research*, 28, No. 4 (1979).

9. U.S., Department of Agriculture, *America's Soil and Water*, p. 14.

10. David Pimentel, et. al., "Land Degradation: Effects of Food and Energy Resources," *Science*, October 8, 1976, pp. 149-155. According to Pimentel, continuous corn culture results in a soil loss of about 20 tons per acre; or 40,000 pounds per acre. 1 acre yields 91 bushels or 5,096 pounds of corn. $40,000 \div 5,096 = 7.8$ lbs. soil lost for each pound of corn produced.

11. U.S., Department of Agriculture, *Basis Statistics*, table 16, The highest sheet and rill erosion losses for cropland in the conterminous United States are in Alabama, Iowa, Kentucky, Mississippi, Missouri and Tennessee. At present erosion rates, 1 inch of topsoil will be eroded in these states in 18, 16, 19, 15, 14 and 11 years respectively.

12. Pimentel, "Land Degradation," p. 150.

13. "Our Thinning Soil," *Land Resource Use and Protection,* Report No. 38. (Ames: Iowa State University, 1975), p. 1.
14. Pimentel, "Land Degradation," p. 154.
15. Sampson, "The Ethical Dimension," p. 91.
16. W. E. Larson, "Protecting the Soil Resource Base," *Journal of Soil and Water Conservation,* 36, No. 1 (1981), pp. 13-16. Calculations are based on 8,000 lbs. of nitrogen and 2,000 lbs. of phosphorous per acre/foot, and May 1981 average prices for nitrogen and phosphorus.
17. D. E. McCormack and W. E. Larson, "A Values Dilemma: Standards for Soil Quality Tomorrow," *Economics, Ethics, Ecology: Roots of Productive Conservation,* ed. Walter E. Jeske (Ankeny: Soil Conservation Society of America, 1981), p. 393.
18. Total soil loss due to erosion = 6.42 billion tons. Assuming 6 inches of topsoil per acre = 960 tons, $(6.42 \times 10^9) \div 960 =$ 6,687,500 acres productive equivalent. At $1,000 per acre, this equals $6,687,500,000 or $6.6 billion.
19. 6.42 billion tons of soil $\times$ $9.00/ton = $57.78 billion.
20. National Association of Dredging Contractors and U.S. Army Corps of Engineers, 1979 figures, personal communication.
21. "Our Thinning Soil," p. 2.
22. McCormack and Larson, "A Values Dilemma," p. 402, 1975 figures updated to 1981 by Bureau of Labor Statistics, Washington, D.C., personal communication.
23. "Our Thinning Soil," p. 2.
24. R. P. Beasley, *Erosion and Sediment Pollution Control* (Ames: Iowa State University Press, 1972), p. 19.
25. *National Agricultural Lands Study,* (Washington, D.C.: National Agricultural Lands Study, 1981), Executive Summary, Final Report, p. 1.
26. Sampson, "The Ethical Dimension," p. 93.
27. R. I. Dideriksen, A. R. Hidlebaugh, and K. O. Schmude, "Trends in Agricultural Land Use," *Farmland, Food and the Future,* p. 22.
28. 4.88 billion tons of soil lost from cropland, pastureland and rangeland due to sheet, rill and wind erosion has a productive equivalent of 5 million acres per year, or 13,698 acres per day, or 21 sq. miles per day. 3 million acres of cropland lost to development per year is 8,219 acres per day, or 12.8 sq. miles per day. 21 + 12.8 = 34 sq. miles per day.
29. Erosion from cropland = 2.82 billion tons (*1980 Appraisal, Part I*), or the productive equivalent of 2,937,500 acres per year, or 8,047,945 acres per day, or 12.6 miles per day. Cropland

loss to development = 12.8 sq. miles per day. 12.6 + 12.8 = 25.4 sq. miles of cropland potential lost per day due to erosion and development.

1 acre of land will produce enough calories to provide 16 people with a minimum diet for a year, Neil Sampson, *Farmland or Wasteland, A Time to Choose* (Emmaus: Rodale, 1981, p. 300). 25.4 × 640 acres/sq. mile = 16,256 acres × 16 = 260,096 people.

30. 16,256 acres cropland potential lost per day, 16,256 × 365 = 5.9 million acres/year. 1980 corn production = 91 bushels/acre (*Agricultural Outlook*, August 1981, A0-68, pp. 28, 37). $(5.9 \times 10^6) \times 91 = (536.9 \times 10^6)$ bushels × \$3.17 (1980 price received by farmer) = \$1.7 billion.

These production calculations are conservative. The productive capabilities of rangeland and pastureland have not been included in the above calculations.

31. Roy L. Donahue, Raymond W. Miller, John C. Shickluna, *Soils, An Introduction to Soils and Plant Growth*. (Englewood Cliffs: Prentice-Hall Inc., 1977), p. 142.

32. Kathryn A. Zeimetz, *Growing Energy, Land for Biomass Farms*, U.S., Department of Agriculture, Economic Report No. 425, (Washington, D.C.: Government Printing Office), pp. 12-14.

33. "Gasohol, A Technical Memorandum," U.S. Office of Technology Assessment (Washington, D.C.: Government Printing Office, 1979), p. 38.

34. J. Dixon Esseks, "Non-urban Competition for Farmland," *Farmland, Food and the Future*, p. 60.

35. Neil Sampson, "Energy: New Kinds of Competition for Land," *Economics, Ethics, Ecology*, p. 337.

36. Esseks, "Non-urban Competition for Farmland," p. 60.

37. Sampson, "Energy: New Kinds of Competition for Land," p. 334.

38. Dideriksen, et. al., "Trends in Agricultural Land Use," p. 23.

39. Esseks, "Non-urban Competition for Farmland," pp. 58, 59.

40. Beasley, p. 4.

41. "To Protect Tomorrows Food Supply, Soil Conservation Needs Priority Attention," Report to the Congress by the Comptroller General (Washington, D.C.: Government Printing Office, 1977), p. 28.

42. Remarks prepared for delivery by Secretary of Agriculture John R. Block, before the National Agricultural Lands Conference, Chicago, Illinois, February 10, 1981.

Monoculture

1. *Genetic Vulnerability of Major Crops* (Washington, D.C.: National Academy of Sciences, 1972), p. 8.
2. Jack R. Harlan, "Crop Monoculture and the Future of American Agriculture," *The Future of American Agriculture as a Strategic Resource* (Washington, D.C.: The Conservation Foundation, 1980), p. 1.
3. P.R. Mooney, *Seeds of the Earth* (Ottawa: International Coalition for Development Action, 1979), 3. 4.
4. U.S., Department of Agriculture, *Agricultural Statistics, 1980* (Washington, D.C.: Government Printing Office, 1980), p. 443.
5. *Genetic Vulnerability*, pp. 286, 287.
6. Jack R. Harlan, *Crops and Man* (Madison, American Society of Agronomy, Inc. 1975), p. 257.
7. *Genetic Vulnerability*, p. 302.
8. Harlan, "Crop Monoculture," p. 11.
9. "A New Kind of Drought," *The New York Times*, 4 August, 1980.
10. "Vanishing Varieties," *Horticulture*, 57, No. 5 (1979), p. 12.
11. *Genetic Vulnerability*, p. 301.
12. *Report of The National Agricultural Research and Extension Users Board* (Washington, D.C.: Government Printing Office, 1980), p. 6.
13. "The Second Green Revolution," *Business Week*, 25 August 1980. p. 92F.
14. Harlan, "Crop Monoculture," p. 8.
15. Bill Humphries, "Genetic Uniformity in Crops Poses Threat to World's Food Supply," *Research and Farming*, Winter-Spring, 1979.
16. Mooney, p. 38.
17. Ibid., pp. 60, 61.
18. Jack Doyle, Letter to Congressman Kiki de la Garza, 7 March, 1980.
19. Mooney, p. 58.
20. Jack Doyle, *Testimony before the Subcommittee on Department Investigations*, 22 April 1980, (Washington, D.C.: Environmental Policy Center, 1980), p. 7.
21. Mooney, p. 67.
22. Doyle, *Testimony*, p. 4.

Energy

1. U.S., Department of Energy, *U.S. Crude Oil and Natural Gas*

Reserves, 1978 Annual Report, September 1980, pp. 7, 8, 10. U.S., Department of Energy, *Monthly Energy Review,* September 1981, (Washington, D.C.: Government Printing Office, 1981), p. 8.

2. U.S., Department of Energy, *Monthly Energy Review,* September 1981, (Washington, D.C.: U.S. Government Printing Office, 1981), p. 3.
3. W.J. Chancellor, "Western Perspective," *American Vegetable Grower,* Vol. 27, No. 11, November 1979, p. 72.
4. Ibid.
5. Keith Abercrombie, "Which Energy Crisis?" *CERES,* FAO Review of Agriculture and Development, FAO Rome, Italy, September-October 1978, p. 15.
6. David Pimentel. et. al., "Energy and Land Constraints in Food Protein Production," *Science,* Vol. 190, November 21, 1975, p. 758.
7. U.S., Department of Agriculture, *1979 Handbook of Agricultural Charts,* Handbook #561, p. 34.
8. The Center for Agricultural and Rural Development, *U.S. Agricultural Production Under Limited Energy Supplies, High Energy Prices, and Expanding Agricultural Exports,* (Iowa State University, Ames, Iowa, 1976), p. 43; U.S., Department of Energy, *Monthly Energy Review,* September 1981, (Washington, D.C.: U.S. Government Printing Office, 1981) pp. 3, 32 and National Energy Information Center, Washington, D.C., personal communication.
9. U.S., Department of Agriculture, *Energy and U.S. Agriculture: 1974 and 1978,* ESCS, Statistical Bulletin No. 632, April 1980, p. 1.
10. James Williams, Deputy Secretary of Agriculture, speaking before the Senate Energy and Natural Resources Committee on February 6, 1980 in *The Energy Consumer,* U.S., Department of Energy, December 1980/January 1981. Special Edition, p. 18.
11. Chancellor, op. cit., p. 72.
12. U.S., Department of Energy, *Agriculture and Food Processes Branch Program Summary Document,* June 1980, (Washington, D.C.: U.S. Government Printing Office, 1980), p. 12.
13. U.S. Department of Commerce, *U.S. Agricultural Production Under Limited Energy Supplies, High Energy Prices, and Expanding Agricultural Exports,* November 1976, Iowa State University, Ames, Iowa, NTIS PB—282 891, pp. 5-6.
14. John S. and Carol E. Steinhart, "Energy Use in the U.S. Food System," *Science,* Vol. 184, 19 April 1974, p. 309.
15. John A. Barton, *Transportation Fuel Requirements in the*

Food and Fiber System, U.S., Department of Agriculture, Agricultural Economic Report No. 444, January, 1980, p. ii.

16. U.S., Department of Agriculture, *Fruit & Vegetable Truck Cost Report for August 1981*, Vol. 3, No. 8.

17. "Fruit and Vegetable Truck Rate Report for Tuesday September, 22, 1981," *Food Transport Week*, September 28, 1981, p. 8.

18. "Fuel Priority a 'Must' for Food Field," Food Marketing Institute, *Supermarket News*, August 10, 1981, p. 2.

19. Jim Hardcastle, "Priming the Pump," *Science*, Vol. 2, No. 1. Jan/Feb, 1981, p. 61.

20. Energy and Defense Project, *Energy Vulnerability and War*, Wilson Clark, Project Director, December 1980, p. 110.

Mineral Base

1. John D. Buffington and Jerrold H. Zar, "Realistic and Unrealistic Energy Conservation Potential in Agriculture," In William Lockeretz, ed., *Agriculture and Energy*, (New York: Academic Press, 1977), p. 697.

2. U.S., Department of Agriculture, *Commercial Fertilizers, Consumption for Year Ended June 30, 1980* Economics and Statistics Service, Crop Reporting Board, November 1980, p. 4.

3. Ibid., p. 4. Total primary nutrient content ÷ 413 million acres.

4. Stanford Research Institute, *U.S. Agriculture: Potential Vulnerabilities*, January 1969, p. 78.

5. U.S., Department of Agriculture, *The Fertilizer Supply, Nitrogen Phosphate Potash 1979-80*, Agricultural Stabilization and Conservation Service, April 1980, pp. 1, 3, 7.

6. General Accounting Office, *Phosphates: A Case Study of a Valuable, Depleting Mineral In America*, Report to the Congress by the Comptroller General, November 30, 1979, p. 32.

7. U.S., Department of Agriculture, *The Fertilizer Supply*, op. cit., p. 7.

8. General Accounting Office, *Phosphates: A Case Study of a Valuable, Depleting Mineral in America*, op. cit. p. i.

9. Ibid., p. 6.

10. Ibid., p. 14.

11. U.S., Department of Agriculture, Agricultural Stabilization and Conservation Service, personal communication, data from table to be published in 1982.

12. Lee Smith, "Armand Hammer and the Phosphate Puzzle," *Fortune*, April 7, 1980, pp. 48-51.

13. National Academy of Sciences, "Supporting Papers: World Food and Nutrition Study," Vol. I Resources for Agriculture, 1977, p. 174.

14. U.S., Bureau of Mines, *Mineral Facts and Problems*, Bulletin 667, 1975 edition, (Washington, D.C.: Government Printing Office, 1976), p. 757.
15. National Energy Information Center, personal communication, October 30, 1981. 117,000 cu.ft. natural gas/year/house ÷ 12 months = 9750 cu.ft./mo. 38,000 ÷ 9750 = 3.89 mos.
16. W.J. Chancellor and J.R. Gross, "Balancing Energy and Food Production, 1975-2000," *Science*, 16 April 1976, Vol. 192, #4236, pp. 213-218.
17. Pennsylvania State University, *Energy Use and the Food System*, Special Circular 246, College of Agriculture Extension Service, University Park, Pennsylvania, p. 5.
18. Ibid.
19. U.S., Bureau of Mines, op. cit., p. 758.
20. U.S., Department of Agriculture, *The Fertilizer Supply*, op. cit., p. 16.
21. Ibid., p. 2.
    U.S., Department of Agriculture, *Agricultural Prices, Annual Summary 1980*, Crop Reporting Board, Economics and Statistics Service, (Washington, D.C.: Government Printing Office, June 1981), pp. 132-133.
22. U.S., Department of Agriculture, *The Fertilizer Supply*, op. cit., p. 7.
23. U.S., Department of Commerce, *Statistical Abstract of the United States 1979*, Bureau of the Census, (Washington, D.C.: Government Printing Office, 1980), p. 765.
24. U.S., Bureau of Mines, op. cit., p. 864.
25. Ibid., p. 867-868.
26. Cecil H. Wadleigh, *Wastes in Relation to Agriculture and Forestry*, U.S., Department of Agriculture, Miscellaneous Publication No. 1065 (Washington, D.C.: Government Printing Office).

Environmental Impacts

1. Theodore R. Eichers, *Farm Pesticide Economic Evaluation, 1981*, U.S., Department of Agriculture, Economics and Statistics Service, Agricultural Economic Report No. 464 (Washington, D.C.: Government Printing Office, 1981), pp. 3-5.
2. U.S., Department of Agriculture, *Commercial Fertilizers, Consumption for Year Ended June 30, 1981* (Washington, D.C.: Government Printing Office, 1980), p. 4. Cultivated cropland calculated at 413,000,000 acres. 1980 fertilizer consumption of primary nutrients = 22,951,800 tons, or 45,903,600,000 lbs. 45,903,600,000 ÷ 413,000,000 = 111.14 lbs. per acre.

3. David Pimental, et. al., "Environmental and Social Costs of Pesticides: A Preliminary Assessment," *Oikos*, 34, No. 2 (1980), pp. 126-140.
4. Cecil H. Wadleigh, *Wastes in Relation to Agriculture and Forestry*, U.S., Department of Agriculture, Miscellaneous Publication No. 1065 (Washington, D.C.: Government Printing Office, 1968), pp. 5, 15, 21.
5. R.C. Whitten, et. al., "Nitrogen Fertilizer and Stratospheric Ozone: Latitudinal Effects," *Nature*, 10 January 1980, p. 191.
6. J.F. Copplestone, "A Global View of Pesticide Safety," *Pesticide Management and Insecticide Resistance*, ed. David L. Watson and A.W.A. Brown (New York: Academic Press, 1977), p. 149.
7. Pimentel, "Environmental and Social Costs," p. 128.
8. Robert C. Patten, "Occupational Diseases of the American Farmer," *Virginia Medical*, 108, No. 5 (1981), p. 339.
9. "Malaria and the Green Revolution," *Science News*, 120, No. 14 (1981), p. 213.
10. Pimentel, "Environmental and Social Costs," p. 135.
11. Eichers, p. 5.
12. David Pimentel, et. al., "Benefits and Costs of Pesticide Use in U.S. Food Production," *Bioscience*, 28, No. 12 (1978), p. 772.

Water

1. Lorus J. Milne and Margery Milne. "Nor Any Drop to Drink." *Country Journal*, August 1980, p. 38.
2. Lawrence Farber. "Guess What We're Not Going to Run Out Of? *Next*, Premier Issue, 1979, p. 49.
3. Kenneth D. Frederick. "Irrigation and the Future of American Agriculture," in *The Future of American Agriculture As a Strategic Resource*, ed. Sandra S. Batie and Robert G. Healy, (Washington, D.C.: Conservation Foundation, 1980), p. 167.
4. U.S., Department of Agriculture, *Soil and Water Resources Conservation Act, Summary of Appraisal, Parts I and II, and Program Report*, Review Draft, 1980, p. 21.
5. Kenneth D. Frederick, pp. 157-158.
6. General Accounting Office. "Ways to Resolve Critical Water Resources Issues Facing the Nation." Report CED 79-87, April 27, 1979, p. 19.
7. Kenneth D. Frederick, p. 166.
8. General Accounting Office. "Water Resources and the Nation's Water Supply." Report CED 79-69, April 13, 1979, p. 55.

9. U.S., Department of Agriculture. *Soil and Water Resources Conservation Act, Appraisal 1980.* Review Draft, Part II, 1980, pp. 3-117.
10. U.S., Department of Agriculture. *Soil and Water Resources Conservation Act, Summary of Appraisal,* p. 9.
11. Kenneth D. Frederick. p. 170. U.S., Department of Commerce, Bureau of Census. *1978 Census of Agriculture,* Vol. 1, Part 51, State Summary Data, Table 11, (Washington, D.C.: Government Printing Office, July 1981), p. 134.
11a. U.S., Department of Commerce, Bureau of the Census. *1978 Census of Agriculture,* Vol. 1, Part 51, State Summary Data, Table 11, (Washington, D.C.: Government Printing Office, July 1981), p. 134.
12. Kenneth D. Frederick, pp. 168-169.
13. U.S., Department of Agriculture. *Soil and Water Resources Conservation Act, Appraisal 1980,* pp. 3-135.
14. Kathleen K. Wiegner. "The water crisis: It's almost here." *Forbes,* August 20, 1979, p. 59.
15. Thomas Y. Canby. "Water, Our Most Precious Resource." *National Geographic,* August 1980, vol. 158, No. 2., pp. 159-160.
16. General Accounting Office, "Ground Water: An Overview." Report CED 77-69, June 21, 1977, p. 15.
17. Kathleen K. Wiegner, p. 60.
18. General Accounting Office. "Ground Water: An Overview," p. 15.
19. Ibid.
20. General Accounting Office. "Water Resources and the Nation's Water Supply," p. 56.
21. Kathleen K. Wiegner, p. 59.
22. Lorus J. Milne and Margery Milne. p. 39.
23. Kenneth D. Frederick, p. 182.
24. Ibid.
25. Kenneth D. Frederick, p. 182.
26. Joel Grossman. "A Low-Sodium Diet for Irrigated Soils." *The New Farm,* Vol. 2, No. 7, November-December, 1980, pp. 36-37.
27. Robert P. Ambroggi. "Water." *Scientific American,* September, 1980, p. 106.
28. Gardens For All. "Food Gardening: A Step Toward a Positive Food Future." May 28, 1980, Section I.
29. Ed Magnuson. "The Poisoning of America." *Time,* September 22, 1980, p. 58.
30. "How bad is it? Believe it or not, we still don't know." *National Wildlife,* Vol. 17, No. 2, February-March, 1979, p. 30.
31. Elmer Staats. Testimony before the Subcommittee on Over-

sight and Review, House Committee on Public Works and Transportation, July 17, 1979, p. 4.

32. Carol Keough. *Water Fit to Drink.* (Emmaus, PA: Rodale Press, 1980.)
33. Ed Magnuson, p. 63.
34. Carol Keough, p. 25.
35. Elmer Staats, p. 2.
36. General Accounting Office. "Water Quality Management Planning Is Not Comprehensive And May Not Be Effective For Many Years." Report CED-78-167, December 11, 1978, p. 2.
37. Elmer Staats, p. 6.
38. General Accounting Office. "Water Quality Management. . ." p. 2.
39. General Accounting Office. "National Water Quality Goals Cannot Be Attained Without More Attention to Pollution From Diffused or 'Nonpoint' Sources." Report CED-78-6, December 20, 1977, p. 14.
40. Eckardt C. Beck. "User, Beware." *New York Times,* Monday, June 30, 1980.
41. Ed Manuson, p. 66.
42. Ibid.
43. Eckardt C. Beck
44. Ed Magnuson, p. 60.
45. Carol Keough, p. 23.
46. Ibid., p. 22.

Climate

1. R.H. Shaw, "Climate Change and the Future of American Agriculture," *The Future of American Agriculture As a Strategic Resource,* (Washington, D.C.: Conservation Foundation, 1980), p. 252.
2. Stephen H. Schneider and Richard L. Temkin, "Climate Change and Human Affairs," *Climatic Change,* ed. John Gribbin, (Cambridge: Cambridge University Press, 1978), p. 236.
3. Sir Fred Hoyle, "The Next Ice Age," *The London Times Sunday Times Magazine,* 7 June, 1981.
4. F. Kenneth Hare, "Climate and Agriculture: The Uncertain Future," *Journal of Soil and Water Conservation,* Vol. 35, No. 3, May-June, 1980, p. 114.
5. R.H. Shaw, "Climate Change," p. 257.
6. *Climate and Food,* (Washington, D.C.: National Academy of Sciences, 1976), p. 14.
7. Central Intelligence Agency, *A Study of Climatological*

Research As It Pertains to Intelligence Problems, August, 1974, p. 1.
8. Eric Pace, "Bad Weather Is Bad Business," *The New York Times*, January 25, 1981.
9. Schneider and Temkin, "Climatic Changes," p. 229.
10. L. Dean Bark, "History of American Droughts," *North American Droughts*, ed. Norman J. Rosenberg (Boulder: Westview Press, Inc., 1978), pp. 13, 19.
11. "Prolonged Drought and Harsh Winters for the Coming Years Seen by Cornell Scientist," Press release issued by News and Features Service of Cornell University, Ithaca, N.Y., 15 May, 1981.
12. Rowan Shirkie, "Climate: Change Is In The Air," *International Research and Development Commission (IRDC) Reports*, Vol. 8, No. 2, June, 1979, p. 25.
13. The Global 2000 Report to the President, A Report Prepared by the Council on Environmental Quality and the Department of State, (Washington, D.C.: Government Printing Office, 1980), p. 51.
14. Bernard E. Dethier, "Problems of a Changing Climate," No. 3 in *A Series of Papers on World Food Issues* (Ithaca: Cornell University, 1979), p. 4.
15. Council on Environmental Quality, *Global Energy Futures and the Carbon Dioxide Problem*, (Washington, D.C.: Government Printing Office, 1981), p. 19.
16. "Climate Cycles Studies in Effort to Curb Drought," *New York Times*, 11 August 1981, p. B4.
17. Council on Environmental Quality, *Global Energy*, p. 3.
18. Walter Sullivan, "Study Finds Warming Trend That Could Raise Sea Levels," *New York Times*, 22 August 1981, p. 1, a.
19. G. Kukla and J. Gavin, "Summer Ice and Carbon Dioxide," *Science*, 214, No. 30 (1981), p. 497.
20. "Scientists Concerned How Rise in CO_2 Will Alter World Weather," *Christian Science Monitor*, 24 March 1981, pp. 14, 15.
21. R.H. Shaw, "Climate Change," p. 254.
22. "Ozone," *SciQuest*, Vol. 53, No. 2, February, 1980, pp. 26, 29.
23. "NAS Calls for Global Aerosol Ban," *Nature*, Vol. 283, 3 January 1981, p. 2.
24. R.H. Shaw, "Climate Change," p. 269.
25. N.R. Glass, P.J. Rennie, "Effects of Acid Precipitation," *Environmental Science and Technology*, 1979, pp. 1350-1355.
26. R.H. Shaw, "Climate Change," p. 271.
27. "Greedy Sahara Devours Land Along Its Borders," *New York Times*, 15 September 1980.

28. Kenneth Bower, "The Ungreening," *OMNI*, December, 1980, p. 70.
29. David Sheridan, *Desertification of the United States*, (Washington, D.C.: Government Printing Office, 1981), pp. 3, 4.

Nutrition/Health

1. Theodore B. Van Itallie, M.D., "Obesity: The American Disease." (Paper presented at a symposium entitled "Role of Nutrition in Chronic Disease.) *Food Technology*, Vol. 33, No. 12, December, 1979, p. 44.
2. Letitia Brewster and Michael F. Jacobson, Ph.D., *The Changing American Diet*. Washington, D.C., Center for Science in the Public Interest, 1978, pp. 4, 30-33.
3. Ibid, pp. 4, 41-42.
4. Ibid., p. 39.
5. Ibid., p. 4.
6. Ibid., p. 47.
7. U.S., Department of Health, Education and Welfare, *Health United States 1979*, Department of Health, Education and Welfare Publication No. (PHS) 80-1232, (Washington, D.C.: Government Printing Office, 1979), pp. 34-35.
8. Ernest Newbrun, D.M.D., Ph.D., "Dietary Carbohydrates: Their Role in Carcinogenicity," *Medical Clinics of North America*, Vol. 63, No. 4, September, 1979, pp. 1069-1086.
9. U.S., Department of Health, Education and Welfare, *Health United States 1979*, pp. 36-37.
10. Ibid., p. 33.
11. George B. Gory, "Food as a Factor in the Etiology of Certain Human Cancers." (Paper presented at a symposium entitled, "Role of Nutrition in Chronic Diseases.") *Food Technology*, Vol. 33, No. 12, December, 1979, p. 48.
12. U.S., Department of Health, Education and Welfare, *Health United States 1979*, pp. 35-36.
13. Ibid., p. 36.
14. *Eating in America*—Dietary Goals for the United States. Report of the Select Committee on Nutrition and Human Needs, U.S. Senate, Massachusetts Institute of Technology Press, Cambridge, Massachusetts, 1977, pp. 3, 71-74.
15. Norton Spritz, M.D., "Review of the Evidence Linking Alcohol Consumption with Liver Disease and Atherosclerotic Disease," *American Journal of Clinical Nutrition*, Vol. 32, December 1979, pp. 2734-2738.
16. *Product Marketing Magazine*, August, 1981, p. 38.

17. J. Michael McGinnis, M.D., "Trends in Disease Prevention: Assessing the Benefits of Prevention," *Bulletin of the New York Academy of Medicine*, Vol. 56, No. 1, Jan/Feb 1980, p. 39.
18. Ibid., p. 39.

Food Processing

1. Edward L. Hampe, Jr., and Merle Wittenberg, *The Lifeline of America*, (New York: McGraw Hill Book Co., 1964), pp. 101-107.
2. U.S., Department of Agriculture, *Cutting Energy Costs: The 1980 Yearbook of Agriculture*, (Washington, D.C.: Government Printing Office, 1980), p. 10.
3. Letitia Brewster, and Michael F. Jacobson, *The Changing American Diet*, (Washington, D.C.: Center for Science in the Public Interest, 1978), p. 30.
4. U.S., Department of Agriculture, *Food Consumption, Prices, and Expenditures*, Economics and Statistics Service, Statistical Bulletin No. 656, (Washington, D.C.: Government Printing Office, 1981), p. 19.
5. Fern Pomerantz, "Food Additives: An Expanding Market in the 80's," *Food Product Development*, 14, No. 12 (1980), p. 36.
6. U.S., Department of Agriculture, *1980 Yearbook*, p. 11.
7. U.S., Department of Agriculture, *Energy Use in the Food System*. Briefing Paper prepared by Economics and Statistics Service, (Washington, D.C.: Economics and Statistics Service, 1979), p. 11.
8. Prices from Weis Market, Allentown, Pennsylvania, October, 1981.
9. "The Effects of Food Processing on Nutritional Values," *Nutritional Reviews*, 33, No. 4 (1975), p. 123.
10. Arnold E. Bender, *Food Processing and Nutrition*, (New York: Academic Press, 1978), p. 175.
11. U.S., General Accounting Office, *Need for More Effective Regulation of Direct Additives to Food*, (Washington, D.C.: Government Printing Office, 1980), p. 1.
12. Fern Pomerantz, p. 36.
13. U.S., General Accounting Office, *More Effective Regulation*, p. 2.
14. Gladys C. Peckham and Jeanne H. Freeland-Graves, *Foundations of Food Preparation*, 4th ed., (New York: Macmillan Publishing Co., Inc., 1979), p. 520.
15. "Boxes, Bottles, Bags, and Cans," *Farmline* 2, No. 8 (1981), p. 9.
16. Anthony E. Gallo and John M. Connor, "Packaging in Food Marketing," *National Food Review*, Spring, 1981, NFR-14, U.S.,

Department of Agriculture, Economics and Statistics Service, pp. 10-13.

17. John A. Barton and Thomas J. Lutton, *Energy Accounting in the Food Processing Industry,* U.S., Department of Agriculture, Economics and Statistics Service, ESCS-51, (Washington, D.C.: Government Printing Office, 1975), p. 2.

18. David Pimentel and Marsha Pimentel, *Food, Energy and Society,* (New York: John Wiley and Sons, 1979), p. 122.

Fisheries

1. Frederick W. Bell, *Food from the Sea: The Economics and Politics of Ocean Fisheries,* (Boulder, Colorado: Westview Press, 1978), p. 22.

2. U.S., Department of Commerce, *Fisheries of the United States, 1980,* Current Fishery Statistics No. 8100; National Marine Fisheries Service, National Oceanic and Atmospheric Administration, p. x1, 6 (Prepared by the Resource Statistics Division, Washington, D.C., April 1981).

3. Ibid., pp. 86, 94.

4. Ibid., p. 6.

5. U.S., Bureau of the Census, *Statistical Abstracts of the United States,* 1980, 101st ed., (Washington, D.C.: Government Printing Office, 1980), pp. 6, #743.

6. Bell, *Food From the Sea: The Economics and Politics of Ocean Fisheries,* p. 195.

7. U.S., Bureau of the Census, *Statistical Abstract of the United States, 1980,* p. 742.

8. U.S., Department of Commerce, *Fisheries,* pp. 1-4.

9. Bell, *Food From the Sea: The Economics and Politics of Ocean Fisheries,* p. 85.

10. Robert C. Baker, "Fish, A Wasted Resource," *New York's Food and Life Sciences,* 2, No. 4 (1978), pp. 12, 13.

11. David Pimental and Marsha Pimental, *Food, Energy, and Society* (New York, New York, John Wiley and Sons, 1979), p. 104.

12. U.S. fish catch for human consumption (1980) 3.654 $\times$ 10^9 lbs. $\times$ .076 (percentage useable protein) $= 277,704,000$ or 5.0376×10^{11} kcal protein; 27 kcal fuel $\times$ 5.0377 $\times$ 10^{11} = 1.360168 $\times$ 10^{13} kcal fuel or 389,175,577 gallons of fuel or $412,526,112.00 at $1.06 per gallon.

13. U.S., Department of Commerce, *Fisheries,* pp. 10, 11.

14. Pimentel, *Food, Energy, and Society,* p. 104.

15. According to Pimentel, p. 108, Lobster fishing requires 192 kcal

of fuel per kcal lobster protein produced. 1 gallon of diesel fuel = 34,950 kcal. 34,950 ÷ 192 = 182 kcal lobster protein output per gallon fuel input. 182 kcal ÷ 4 (=45.5 g. protein) ÷ .19 (239.47 g. edible weight) ÷ .29 (=825.913 g. mind weight including shell) ÷ 453.51 = 1.82 lbs. lobster per gallon diesel fuel.

16. U.S., Environmental Protection Agency, *Fish Kills Caused by Pollution: Fifteen Year Summary 1961-1975*, (Washington, D.C.: Government Printing Office, 1979), p. 11.
17. Herbert W. Newkirk, ed. *Environmental Effects of Energy Production and Utilization in the U.S.*, (Washington, D.C.: Government Printing Office, 1976), I, p. 264.
18. Bell, *Food From the Sea: The Economics and Politics of Ocean Fisheries*, p. 218.
19. Ibid., p. 211.
20. U.S., Department of State, *Global Future*, pp. 108, 109.

Forest Resources

1. *Renewable Natural Resources*, (Washington, D.C.: American Forestry Association, 1980), p. 40.
2. *Green America*, No. 26, (Washington, D.C.: American Forest Institute, 1980).
3. *Renewable Natural Resources*, p. 42.
4. U.S., Department of Agriculture, *The Outlook for Timber in the United States*, Forest Resource Report No. 20, (Washington, D.C.: Government Printing Office, 1973), p. 129.
5. U.S., Department of Agriculture, *Agricultural Statistics, 1980*, (Washington, D.C.: Government Printing Office, 1980), p. 542.
6. Robert H. Stone and Robert B. Phelps, "Prospective U.S. Wood Use Situation", *Forest Products Journal*, 30, No 10 (1980), p. 51.
7. Norman Myers, "The Hamburger Connection: How Central America's Forests Become North America's Hamburgers", *Ambio*, 10, No. 1 (1981), p. 3.
8. Hazel R. Delcourt, "The Virtue of Forests, Virgin and Otherwise," *Natural History*, 90, No. 6 (1981), p. 33.
9. *The Green America Book*, (Washington, D.C.: American Forest Institute, 1980), n.p.
10. Robert E. Jones and James S. Paxton, "The 296 Million Acre Myth", *American Forests*, 1980, p. 6.
11. *The Outlook for Timber in the United States*, p. 17.
12. Ibid., p. 53.
13. "Forest Pesticides: An Overview", *Environmental Science and Technology*, 14, No. 10 (1980), p. 1165.

14. U.S., Department of Agriculture, Soil Conservation Service, Basic Statistics, 1977 National Resources Inventory revised 1980, (Washington, D.C.: U.S., Department of Agriculture, 1980), Table 17.

Urban Food Systems

1. *Washington Food Review*, 15 August 1981, p. 4.
2. U.S., Department of Commerce, Bureau of Census, *Statistical Abstract of the United States, 1980*, 101st ed., (Washington, D.C.: Government Printing Office, 1980), p. 25.
3. U.S., Department of Agriculture, *Agricultural Statistics 1980*, (Washington, D.C.: Government Printing Office, 1980), p. 554. Per capita consumption of food = 1,463 lbs. × 1,755,000 (population of Philadelphia) = 2,567,565,000 lbs./year, or 7,034,000 lbs./day.
4. Assuming average truckload of food = 40,000 lbs. 7,034,000 ÷ 40,000 = 175.85.
5. *The Pennsylvania Food System: Crash or Self-Reliance?* Study by The Cornucopia Project, (Emmaus: Rodale Press, 1981), p. 3. Per capita consumption of food = $1,023 × 1,755,000 (population of Philadelphia) = $1,795,400,000.
6. U.S., Department of Agriculture, *1980 Handbook of Agricultural Charts*, Agricultural Handbook No. 574, (Washington, D.C.: Government Printing Office, 1980), p. 39. Transportation makes up 5.3% of consumer expenditures for food. $1,795,400,000 × .053 = $9.52 × 10^7 spent on transporting food to Philadelphia.
7. *The Pennsylvania Food System*, p. 3.
8. U.S., Department of Commerce, Bureau of the Census, *1978 Census of Agriculture*, Vol. 1, Parts 1-50, Table 1, County Summary Data, (Washington, D.C.: Government Printing Office, July, 1981).
9. Ibid., Table 10.
10. U.S., Government Accounting Office, *Preserving America's Farmland—A Goal The Federal Government Should Support*, A Report to the Congress, (Washington, D.C.: Government Printing Office, 1979), pp. 3, 4.

Food Assistance

1. "Census Bureau Finds Increase in Poverty," *Community Nutrition Institute (CNI) Weekly Report*, Vol. XI, No. 35, September 3, 1981, p. 5.
1a. *Allentown Call Chronicle*, 16 December 1980, Virginia Morell, "Why Food Costs So Much," *New Age*, May, 1981, p. 50.

2. "USDA To Revise Thrifty Food Plan," *CNI Weekly Report*, Vol. X, No. 40, October 9, 1980, p. 3.
3. "Federal Domestic Food Assistance Programs—A Time for Assessment and Change," United States General Accounting Office (U.S.G.A.O.), June 13, 1978, p. 88.
4. Ibid., pp. 1, 2.
5. Marilyn Stackhouse, Food and Nutrition Service, U.S., Department of Agriculture, (202) 447-8140 personal communication.
6. Ibid.
7. The Food Law Project, "New York City Fact Sheet on Proposed Federal Budget Cuts," New York, New York, March, 1981, p. 3.
8. "Facts About Food Stamps," *CNI Weekly Report*, Vol. XI, No. 10, March 5, 1981, p. 5.
9. Steven V. Roberts, "As It Grows, Food Stamp Program Sprouts Debate," *New York Times*, July 29, 1979.
10. Ibid.
11. The Children's Foundation, "Food Stamp Fact Sheet," (Washington, D.C.: The Children's Foundation, 1981), p. 2.
12. Stackhouse, op. cit.
13. Robert Rizek, U.S., Department of Agriculture, (202) 436-8474, personal communication.
14. The Food Law Project, "Poor Kids Don't Get Four Meals a Day," New York, New York, undated, p. 1.
15. The Food Law Project, "Food Stamp Facts," New York, New York, March, 1981, p. 1.
16. *Progressive Grocer*, Vol. 60, No. 4, April, 1981, pp. 115-116.
17. 42% of proposed $1.6 billion cutback = $672 million.
18. Food Research and Action Center (FRAC), "Legislative Update," Washington, D.C.: August 7, 1981, p. 1.
19. "USDA Concedes Rise in Food Stamp Costs," *CNI Weekly Report*, Vol. XI, No. 33, August 13, 1981, p. 2.
20. Roberts, op. cit.
21. FRAC, "Final Results," op cit.
22. "Feeding Programs Meet 'Barest Needs'," *CNI Weekly Report*, Vol. X, No. 17, April 24, 1980, p. 3.
23. Former Assistant Secretary of Agriculture, Carol Tucker Foreman, personal communication.
24. CNI Weekly Report, March 5, 1981, p. 5, op. cit.

International Dimensions

1. U.S., Department of Agriculture, "Food Spending and Income," *National Food Review*, Spring, 1981, p. 4.

2. U.S., Department of Agriculture, *Agricultural Statistics 1980* (Washington, D.C.: Government Printing Office, 1980), p. 561, Table 773. With imports valued at $16,187,000,000 when entering the country, and assuming a minimum 50 percent markup to retail price, the actual figure would be about 12 percent of our $273.3 billion food bill for the year 1979.

3. Ibid., p. 567, Table 781 and p. 562, Table 775.

4. "The Two Faces of Pesticide Exports," *The Boomerang Booklet* (Emmaus, PA: Rodale Press, 1980), p. 3.

5. Frances Moore Lappe, Joseph Collins and Cary Fowler, *Food First Beyond the Myth of Scarcity,* (Boston: Houghton Mifflin Company, 1979), p. 408.

6. Ibid., p. 203.

7. Ibid., pp. 182-185.

8. David Pimentel, *Food, Energy and the Future of Society* (Boulder, Colo.: Colorado Associated University Press, 1980), p. 32.

9. R. Jeffrey Smith, "U.S. Beginning to Act on Banned Pesticides," *Science,* June 29, 1979, p. 1393.

10. Norman Myers, "The Hamburger Connection: How Central America's Forest Become North America's Hamburgers," *Ambio,* 10 No. 1, (1981), pp. 5-6.

11. U.S., Department of Agriculture, *A Time to Choose: Summary Report on the Structure of Agriculture* (Washington, D.C.: Government Printing Office, 1981), p. 139.

12. "Increased Farm Exports Benefit U.S. Consumers," *Lancaster Farming,* 3 January 1981, p. A17.

13. Projected exports are $48 billion, against projected imports of $21 billion, leaving a $27 billion surplus.

14. Ann Crittenden, "U.S. Grain-Export Drive Stirs Doubts," *New York Times,* 1 September 1981, pp. A1, D6.

15. Ibid.

16. Lauren Soth, "Are America's Farmers 'Exporting' Their Topsoil?" *The Christian Science Monitor,* 3 June 1981, p. 12.

17. U.S., Department of Commerce, Bureau of the Census, *Statistical Abstract of the U.S. 1980,* (Washington, D.C.: Government Printing Office, 1980), p. 713.

18. "Food Supplies at the Crossroads," *Farm Economics,* Pennsylvania State University Cooperative Extension Service, February, 1981.

19. Statement of Frances Moore Lappe Before the Committee on Agriculture, U.S. House of Representatives, *Hearings to Review*

Agricultural Export Issues (San Francisco: Institute for Food and Development Policy, 1981). p. 21.

20. Ann Crittenden, p. D6.
21. Roger Burbach and Patrician Flynn, *Agribusiness in the Americas,* (New York: Monthly Review Press, 1980), p. 64.
22. Lauren Soth, p. 13.
23. Ann Crittenden, p. D6.
24. "FAO Calls World Food Situation Fragile," *Journal of Soil and Water Conservation,* 36, No. 2, March-April (1981), p. 97.
25. Frances Moore Lappe, et al. *Food First,* pp. 31-34, 127.
26. Presidential Commission on World Hunger, *Overcoming World Hunger: The Challenge Ahead* (Washington, D.C., 1980), p. 222.
27. Frances Moore Lappe Statement Before the House Agriculture Committee, p. 8.
28. Ann Crittenden, p. D6.
29. Ibid.
30. U.S., Department of Agriculture, *A Time to Choose,* p. 82.
31. Testimony of Jack Doyle (Washington Representative for the Environmental Policy Center) Before the Subcommittee on Conservation, Credit and Rural Development of The Committee on Agriculture, U.S. House of Representatives, "Agricultural Resources Issues and The 1981 Farm Bill," March 12, 1981, p. 2.
32. National Agricultural Lands Study *Executive Summary Final Report 1981,* (Washington, D.C.: National Agricultural Lands Study, 1981), p. 1.
33. Frances Moore Lappe Statement Before The House Agriculture Committee, pp. 33-34.

Goals of the U.S. Food System

1. *Eating in America, Dietary Goals for the United States,* (Cambridge: The MIT Press, 1977), p. 12.
2. *1980-81 National Gardening Survey,* conducted by the Gallup Organization, Inc., (Burlington: Gardens for All, Inc., 1980), p. 15.
3. There are eight land capability classes that are used to determine a land's ability to grow crops. They range from Class I land, which is best for growing crops, and requires few conservation practices, to Class VIII land which is unsuitable for commercial crop production. Of the 4 classes suitable for cropland (I through IV) all but I require careful management and conservation practices.

4. L.J. Carter, "Soil Erosion: The Problem Persists Despite Billions Spent On It," *Science*, 22 April 1977, p. 409.
5. U.S., Department of Agriculture, *Report and Recommendations on Organic Farming*, (Washington, D.C.: Government Printing Office, 1980), p. 31.
6. "Our Thinning Soil," *Land Resource Use and Protection*, Report No. 38, (Ames: Iowa State University, 1975), p. 5.
7. U.S., Department of Agriculture, *1979 Handbook of Agricultural Charts*, (Washington, D.C.: Government Printing Office, 1979), p. 34.
8. This figure was based on providing the U.S. food system with 12×10^{15} BTUs (3.4×10^{12} kwh) of energy in the form of electricity—the most expensive form of energy. Photovoltaics at .5¢ per peak watt operating 40% of the year were used to figure costs.
8a. In 1981 the U.S. Government spent $85 billion on food. (Personal communication, Daniel Wilson, Office of Federal Procurement, Office of Management and Budget, Washington, D.C.) The Department of Agriculture conservatively estimates that 5.3 percent of the retail cost of food is for transportation, (U.S., Department of Agriculture, *1980 Handbook of Agricultural Charts*, Agricultural Handbook No. 574, (Washington, D.C.: Government Printing Office, 1980), p. 39.)
    $85 billion $\times$ .053 = $4.5 billion
9. U.S., Department of Commerce, Bureau of the Census, *Statistical Abstract of the United States 1980*, (Washington, D.C.: Government Printing Office, 1980), pp. 215, 217, 642, 645, 646, 647.
    a. Total receipts from highways = $34,927 million. Total imposts on users = $22,532 million.
       22,352 ÷ 34,927 = .639 or 64% charged to users.
    b. $10.8 billion (government contracts awarded) ÷ 125.1 billion gallons (fuel used in transportation) = $.09 per gallon.
    c. $56.4 billion (economic loss due to highway accidents) ÷ 125.1 billion gallons = $.45 per gallon.
    d. Pollutant emissions from road vehicles make up half of all air pollutant emissions, therefore, half of the $543 million spent on air pollution control is for road vehicle emissions. 543 ÷ 2 = $227 million ÷ 125.1 billion gallons = $.01 per gallon.
10. R. Neil Sampson, "The Ethical Dimension of Farmland Protection,"

Farmland, Food and the Future, (Ankeny: Soil Conservation Society of America, 1979), p. 97.

11. U.S., Department of Commerce, Bureau of the Census, *Historical Statistics of the United States,* (Washington, D.C.: Government Printing Office, 1975), p. 487.

U.S., Department of Agriculture, *Agricultural Statistics, 1980,* (Washington, D.C.: Government Printing Office, 1980), p. 520.

Appendix

1
Cornucopia Op-Ed Ads

Sixth in a series.

The losing of America.

The United States will lose 26 square miles of its land today.

It will lose another 26 square miles tomorrow, and every day this year.

But not to a foreign power.

We are giving up our land to the ravenous demands of an unrealistic food system. And, before you turn the page, telling youself that land loss is someone else's problem — too remote, too big for you — it *isn't.*

You *can* help to face this dilemma. And help yourself, too.

If you know these facts:

Each time an Iowa farmer grows one pound of corn for you and us, he uses up five to six pounds of topsoil. And in the wheatlands, for each pound harvested, up to 20 pounds of soil disappear — never again to be available for growing food.

In 1980 — and again in 1981 — three million acres of farmlands will be lost to erosion. Five billion tons of topsoil are displaced annually — enough to cover all five boroughs of New York City with a 13½-foot-deep layer of soil.

And while this is going on, each year, another three million acres of agricultural land are lost to development: new homes, factories, and other structures.

Let's concede those three million acres to the requirements of "progress."

But why is it that, in the areas still being farmed, we're eating up more land than food?

Because today's food producers are "burning up" the soil with chemicals in order to maintain high yields. Because, when they over-use chemicals, the soil becomes more vulnerable to wind and water erosion. Because the ways of commerce are now overruling the wisdom of crop rotation. And because modern tractors don't permit the strip cropping and contour plowing that are most effective for preventing erosion.

Man-made blights, these. Symptoms of a food system that is dangerously out of touch with our new world of limited resources. A food system that is headed for disaster, unless we do something about it.

That's not easy to believe. Not with our bumper harvests almost every year, and our grain-clogged warehouses.

But the danger signals are inescapable: We have already lost half of our land. Each day, the U.S. population increases by 5,000 people while the farmlands shrink. And prices soar, because the food system needs more and more expensive energy to operate.

Is there still time? We believe there is.

America *can* produce food at less cost to the consumer, and to the environment. The nation's citizens *don't* have to pay for food today with fertile soil they'll need tomorrow.

That's why we launched *The Cornucopia Project* — a concentrated effort to collect information about the ways the U.S. food system must be restructured to prevent a food crisis.

The information we've already assembled could be of great importance to you, personally, and we'd be pleased to share it. No cost or obligation, of course. Just write: Robert Rodale, Rodale Press, 33 E. Minor St., Emmaus, PA 18049.

RODALE PRESS, INC.
Emmaus, PA 18049

Rodale publishes: *Prevention, Rodale's New Shelter, Organic Gardening, Bicycling, Executive Fitness Newsletter, New Farm,* and *Theatre Crafts,* as well as hardcover and paperback books under the Rodale Books imprint.

Saving America's water.

When Mayor Ed Koch launched his crusade to save water, he enlisted New York City's youngsters.

But, to avoid future water problems across the nation, we would do well to enlist our farmers.

That's because Dad's morning shave and Mom's dishwashing habits have far less impact on water consumption throughout America than they do in New York.

Only about six percent of the country's water resources are used in homes.

About 11 percent goes for industrial or miscellaneous uses.

Agriculture takes all the rest — an astounding 83 percent — much of it for irrigation.

But if the farmers are closer to the water problem than anyone else, they are also closer to the solution. They cannot create water where none exists, of course. But they *can* learn to grow plants that aren't water-guzzlers.

Consider this:

Most of our food today comes from seven plants: wheat, corn, rice, the soybean, the common bean, barley, and the potato — all of which need ample rain. Lacking that, these plants must have irrigation; and this uses up water that, in the future, we'll need for our homes and factories.

Do farmers have to base their crop futures on so few plants that require so much water? No. It's never been necessary. And it's certainly not wise. Especially with so many native plants from dry areas offering a cornucopia of alternatives.

In the Sonoran Desert, for example, Arizona scientists have identified 40 species of wild food plants already being used by residents of the region as food staples.

Several of those Arizona plants produce seeds richer in protein than our common grains. And others produce fruits rich in carbohydrates.

Or, come closer to home. To the Organic Gardening and Farming Research Center, near Maxatawney, PA, where Rodale researchers have been working for eight years to develop an unthirsty plant called amaranth.

The sun-loving amaranth grows waist-high and produces massive seed heads sometimes weighing as much as eight pounds. It is a basic food of American Indians, as well as Aztec and Incan descendants living in remote dry regions. And before long, we expect, you too will be eating amaranth in a wide range of dishes.

In pancakes, cereals, and breads.

In crepes and dumplings and toppings.

Even in snack bars.

It's the good taste of amaranth that has convinced many people of the plant's great potential. Nutritionists are attracted by its high protein content, 15 to 18 percent. And farmers will be interested in our own experience last year: While nearby corn fields withered, our amaranth crop flourished. Without irrigation.

Clearly, this is an ancient crop whose time has come. Again.

And that's good news. For American consumers, and for water-short farmers who must find new ways to produce food — profitably and effectively.

RODALE PRESS, INC.
Emmaus, PA 18049

Rodale publishes: *Prevention, Rodale's New Shelter, Organic Gardening, Bicycling, Executive Fitness Newsletter, The New Farm,* and *Theatre Crafts,* as well as hardcover and paperback books under the Rodale imprint. The company also produces films and television programs.

Twenty-seventh in a series.

Now. A diet that works.

Distance lends enchantment, the poet observed.

And if he hadn't said it almost two hundred years ago, today's vacation-minded city dwellers would say it for him.

But distance—though it's good for the soul and suntan—seldom does any good at all for the food on your dinner table.

Broccoli, which we've mentioned earlier in this series, offers one unhappy example: Most of the 24,000 tons of broccoli consumed annually in the New York area are transported here from the West Coast, 2,700 miles away. From field to market, the shipment usually takes five to seven days—often as much as two weeks.

Yet refrigerated broccoli loses 19 per cent of its vitamin C in just twenty-four hours, 34 per cent in two days.

Asparagus kept in cold storage loses two-thirds of its vitamin C in a week-long trip to the New York consumer. As well as a considerable portion of its vitamins A and B.

And when spinach has spent a week in cold storage, much of its vitamin C is spent, too—29 per cent of it.

That's one of the reasons we propose a new diet for *all* of the people of this region—heavy and thin, rich and poor.

We call it *The Local Diet*—a miracle formula that is unequivocally guaranteed to achieve marvelous reductions for the body politic.

To go on this diet, you need only resolve to buy *fresh, local* foods whenever possible — and to adjust your menus to harmonize with seasonal availabilities in your area.

If you follow the diet faithfully — and get your neighbors to join in — you'll begin to see results almost immediately.

First, you'll reduce energy use.

Right now, with our crazy-quilt pattern of unplanned food growing and unrealistic distribution, the nation needs 500 million gallons of fuel yearly to move fresh fruits and vegetables to market. And more than twice that amount — 1,300 million gallons — to move manufactured food products from processors to warehouses and super-markets.

Next, you'll reduce your vulnerability.

To transportation strikes, to energy crises, and to other unpredictable forces that can suddenly elevate prices and disrupt the normal flow of food into your area. Including, of course, such unfriendly visitors as the Mediterranean fruit fly.

Finally, you'll reduce the severe loss of local revenue that occurs whenever consumers go outside their own area for food supplies.

Estimates indicate that the New York area's dependence on California for broccoli costs our region approximately $85 million each year—money that could remain here if we would grow broccoli here. Similarly, local production of lettuce would save an additional $265 million.

But it's what The Local Diet can *add*, as much as reduce, that makes the most important difference:

Better flavor and more nutrition, often at real savings for the individual.

That's why we urge you to find out what foods are grown near you. Buy them, use them, make them a regular part of your menus.

And we also invite you to write for our free brochure, *The Cornucopia Project*, which gives you a helpful and interesting overview of America's food system — its problems and possibilities, and how they affect you.

For your free copy, please write:
Robert Rodale, *The Cornucopia Project*, Rodale Press, Emmaus, PA 18049.

RODALE PRESS, INC.
Emmaus. PA 18049

Thirty-second in a series.

Nurturing the Garden State.

There's a lot of losing going on these days in New Jersey — Not all of it at the Atlantic City gaming tables.

One thing New Jersey is losing is a firm grip on its title as the Garden State.

The "vegetable basket of the East" is now better known for its refineries, chemical plants, highways, and New York City bedroom communities.

The state that made truck farming a major economic force now imports more than half of its vegetables and 75 per cent of its fruit.

In all, 75 per cent of the food consumed by New Jersey's residents comes from outside the state: 99 per cent of the beef, 86 per cent of the eggs, 74 per cent of the fluid milk and cream, and almost 100 per cent of the poultry.

Inevitably, as all of this food rolls into the state, money flows out.

Last year, New Jerseyites spent only $0.7 billion for locally produced food. They spent more than ten times that amount, $7.3 billion, for imported food. Of this, about 20 per cent stayed with local retailers, and $5.8 billion left the state — a net loss, *each day,* of $15.9 million.

New Jersey's most serious loss, however, isn't money. It's land.

Since 1950, 44 per cent of the state's farmland has vanished.

Much of it has gone to developers. Every two years, an area the size of Newark is lost to high-rises, highways, and shopping centers.

Erosion, too, has claimed a huge amount of nutrient-rich soil: about 5.5 million tons annually, or enough to cover the city of Trenton with a layer more than seven inches deep.

But, as readers of these messages know, New Jersey's plight is not unique. New York, Pennsylvania, and virtually all other states in the Northeast face the same problem. Or soon will.

What is different in New Jersey — and merits the attention of everyone in this area — is what's being done there.

Local groups of farmers, business executives, and private citizens met several years ago to take a realistic look at what was happening to agriculture in the Garden State, and how it could be improved.

They reported their findings to two State departments, Agriculture and Environmental Protection, which subsequently issued the "Grassroots Report: An Agricultural Retention and Development Program for New Jersey."

Don't be put off by the title. Behind the gobbledygook there is a solid, locally initiated plan rooted in the state's strong commitment to sustain and stimulate New Jersey agriculture.

And now, in November, consumers will have their chance to vote on the Farmland Preservation Bond Act, which calls for the state to issue $50 million in bonds to finance the purchase of easements on farmlands and for water and soil conservation projects.

The cost, admittedly, is high. But New Jersey's voters will have the opportunity to decide whether the cost may not be even higher if farmlands continue to disappear and there must be a growing dependence on costly foods from other states.

It's a problem likely to become more common throughout this section of the U.S. So, our Cornucopia Report on New Jersey, just completed, can be important to you wherever you live.

For a free copy, please write to: Robert Rodale, The Cornucopia Project, Rodale Press, Emmaus, PA 18049.

**RODALE
PRESS, INC.**
Emmaus, PA 18049

Rodale publishes: *Prevention, Rodale's New Shelter, Organic Gardening, Bicycling, Executive Fitness Newsletter, The New Farm,* and *Spring,* as well as hardcover and paperback books under the Rodale imprint. The company also produces films and television programs.

2
Background and Acknowledgements

Background and Acknowledgements

The primary aim of The Cornucopia Project is to create an accessible body of information about the U.S. food system that can be used by all individuals and groups seeking to understand and improve that system. We feel that our work is unique, and is needed badly. We have not been able to find any other organization, either public or private, which is doing this kind of work. And it is obvious, because of the tremendous complexity of the food system, that holistic analysis of this kind is needed to understand how the elements of the system interact, and what the result of change in the strength of each element is likely to be.

Some Cornucopia Project studies are on a national scale, such as this report. Others examine the food systems of states. So far, we have completed audits of Pennsylvania, Maine, New York, New Jersey and Michigan. Currently underway are studies of California, Arizona, North Carolina,Florida and Illinois. It is our intention to audit the food systems of all 50 states. In addition to these research reports, The Cornucopia Project distributes a free newsletter to over 25,000 people and issues other reports on various aspects of the food system. Research in progress includes county, neighborhood, family, and industry level food system studies.

The Cornucopia Project has grown out of Rodale Press's over 40 year concern about the problems of the U.S. food system. It was, originally, a response to repeated inquiries about the state of the U.S. food system and what should be done about it. *Empty Breadbasket?: The Coming Challenge to America's Food*

Supply and What We Can Do About It is the response to these inquiries.

The Cornucopia Project has a full time staff of seven people plus three to five interns. It is funded almost entirely by Rodale Press. Small amounts of additional funds have come from symposia and publications. Although a for-profit company, Rodale Press has a long history of funding food system research that has no direct payback to the company, Most, if not all, of this somewhat unorthodox business behavior can be attributed to (or blamed on) the vision and social conscience of Robert Rodale, the Chairman of the Board of this family owned company.

This document, from its inception, has been a group effort. It was launched by an eclectic group of fifteen researchers, editors and management personnel at an intensive two-day seminar held in the Fall of 1979 that I facilitated. Out of this seminar grew not only the initial in-house report which is the foundation of *Empty Breadbasket?*, but the primary impetus and conceptual underpinnings for the entire Cornucopia Project. This group effort was continued by the growing Cornucopia Staff. Ellen Pahl, Tom Dybdahl, Jean Polak, Pat Messing, Ray Wirth and I contributed to the research and writing while Tom Dybdahl copy-edited, Brenda Bortz proofread, Jean Polak, Andrea Cesari, Ellen Pahl, and Pat Messing fact-checked. Sue Campbell and Karen Buchecker typed and retyped the entire document at least a dozen times. Sue Campbell also did many of the charts and graphs, Jean Polak managed to see to it that the production operation went smoothly, and was finished on time, Carol Gladys answered the mail, thereby providing everyone with the time to do their tasks, and I provided a modicum of conceptual leadership. In addition to the already mentioned people, the Recommendations section of *Empty Breadbasket?* benefited from the experience and insights of Robert Rodale, John Haberern, Richard Harwood, George DeVault, Gene Logsdon, Patrick Madden and Sara Ebenreck; and The Cornucopia Project in general received valuable and greatly appreciated feedback in its early formative stages from Wendell Berry, Donnella Meadows, Kenneth Dahlberg, Garth Youngberg and a host of others too numerous to mention. In addition to all these people, three others need special acknowledgement for the pivotal roles they have played in this document and entire Cornucopia Project. The first of these people is John Haberern, the person in charge of research at Rodale Press, who has helped enormously throughout the project's brief history with his constructive insights and untiring support. The second is Richard Harwood, who directs agricultural research at Rodale Press and whose sagacity and guidance in the early stages of *Empty Breadbasket?* helped form its ultimate directions. The third person is Robert Rodale, without whose vision, conceptual leadership, enthusiasm and support this document and The Cornucopia Project would not exist.

—Medard Gabel
Director, The Cornucopia Project